What is Britannica SmartMath?

Encyclopædia Britannica® has worked with educational experts to develop an online adaptive practice product that will encourage and challenge your child to become better in math. *Britannica SmartMath®* has an extensive math curriculum and the program will automatically create individualized learning paths for your child. The program will track your child's strengths and weaknesses in different topics from Grades 1 through 6 and will choose appropriate materials for your child's practice sessions.

The *Britannica SmartMath®* workbook series has been integrated with the online learning program. When a workbook section is completed, your child can earn points that can be applied to the online learning system—allowing the online program to carry your child's math learning to the next level!

35,000 Math Problems
91 Math Topics
Grade 1-6
5 Dimensions in Math

Numbers
Measures
Shapes and Space
Data Handling
Algebra

1 Quality Math Content

SmartMath® content is aligned with the National Council of Teachers of Mathematics standards. All activities are designed to help your child build solid foundations in five general math subjects: Numbers, Measures, Shapes and Space, Data Handling, and Algebra.

2 Online Exercises that Adapt to Your Child

Learning math is more personalized than ever because the *SmartMath®* program tracks your child's strengths and weaknesses in different topics and intuitively adapts the presented material accordingly.

3 Motivated Self-Learning

Britannica SmartMath® wants to make math practice an enjoyable experience. In addition to the special characters and user-friendly interface, children are naturally motivated with special reward badges, progress certificates, and a web leader board.

www.britannicasmartmath.com/workbook

Program Features

Introducing Britannica SmartMath: the world's most advanced math practice system!

DESIGNED FOR THE INDIVIDUAL CHILD!

A little practice every day goes a long way in mathematics. SmartMath makes it easy, interactive, and enjoyable for your child.

▶ **SmartMath Core**
Browse the extensive library of quality math practice questions

▶ **Explore It!**
Explore math concepts with our interactive manipulatives

▶ **My Badges**
Track achievements by topic and print certificates

▶ **My Points & Leader Board**
Earn points on the monthly leader board to encourage self-learning

SMARTMATH IS PARENT-FRIENDLY!

Stay informed about your child's math progress at the convenience of a click. The more you know, the more you can help your child succeed and move to the next level!

▶ **Calendar View**
Monitor your child's login information & practice time

▶ **Report Card**
View your child's progress within each math topic

▶ **Curriculum View**
Track your child's progress according to our curriculum

▶ **Worldwide Comparison!**
Compare your child's progress to other users

▶ **Send Messages**
Personalize words of encouragement and feedback for your child

Practice for Exams!

Varied questions help improve your child's skills in multiple areas: number sense, understanding word problems, logical reasoning, and concept application.

Practice Anytime!

Choose relevant topics and allow your child to practice new math skills while reinforcing critical skills learned at school – just 15 to 30 minutes each day will go a long way!

Practice Wisely!

The SmartMath system tracks your child's success within each math topic. Practice is designed to capitalize on learning strengths and build confidence in weaker areas.

SMARTMATH Curriculum Levels, Dimensions, and Math Topics

Level 1

NUMBERS

- [10] Numbers to 10
- [20] Numbers to 20
- [+/-] Basic Addition & Subtraction
- [100] Numbers to 100
- [+/- 12] Addition & Subtraction I

MEASURES

- [$] Money I
- [🕐] Time I
- [📏] Length & Distance I
- [cm] Length & Distance II

SHAPES AND SPACE

- Straight Lines & Curved Lines
- 2-D Shapes
- 3-D Shapes

Level 2

NUMBERS

- [999] 3-Digit Numbers
- [+/- 123] Addition & Subtraction II
- [+/- 456] Addition & Subtraction III
- [9999] 4-Digit Numbers
- [×] Basic Multiplication
- [÷] Basic Division

MEASURES

- [$] Money II
- [🕐] Time II
- [m] Length & Distance III
- [⚖] Weight

SHAPES AND SPACE

- [▢] Quadrilaterals I
- [∟] Angles I
- [🎲] 3-D Shapes II
- [N] The Four Compass Points

DATA HANDLING

- [📊] Pictograms I

Level 3

NUMBERS

- [99999] 5-Digit Numbers
- [+/- 1234] Addition & Subtraction IV
- [×1] Multiplication I
- [2/24] Division I
- [(+/-) ×÷] Mixed Operations I
- [1/2] Fractions I

MEASURES

- [🕐] Time III
- [24:00] Time IV
- [km] Length & Distance IV
- [⚖] Capacity

SHAPES AND SPACE

- [≠] Parallel & Perpendicular Lines
- [▱] Quadrilaterals II
- [∠] Angles II
- [◁] Triangles

DATA HANDLING

- [📊] Block Graphs
- [📈] Bar Charts I

Level 4

NUMBERS

- [×12] Multiplication II
- [12/24] Division II
- [🔢] Calculators
- [1,2,4 1,2] Multiples & Factors
- [0,24 0,2] Common Multiples & Common Factors
- [+/- ×÷] Mixed Operations II
- [2 1/2] Fractions II
- [0.1] Decimals

MEASURES

- [▢] Perimeter I
- [▦] Area I

SHAPES AND SPACE

- [▱] Quadrilaterals III
- [◪] Fitting & Dissecting Shapes
- [◁] Simple Symmetry

DATA HANDLING

- [📊] Pictograms II

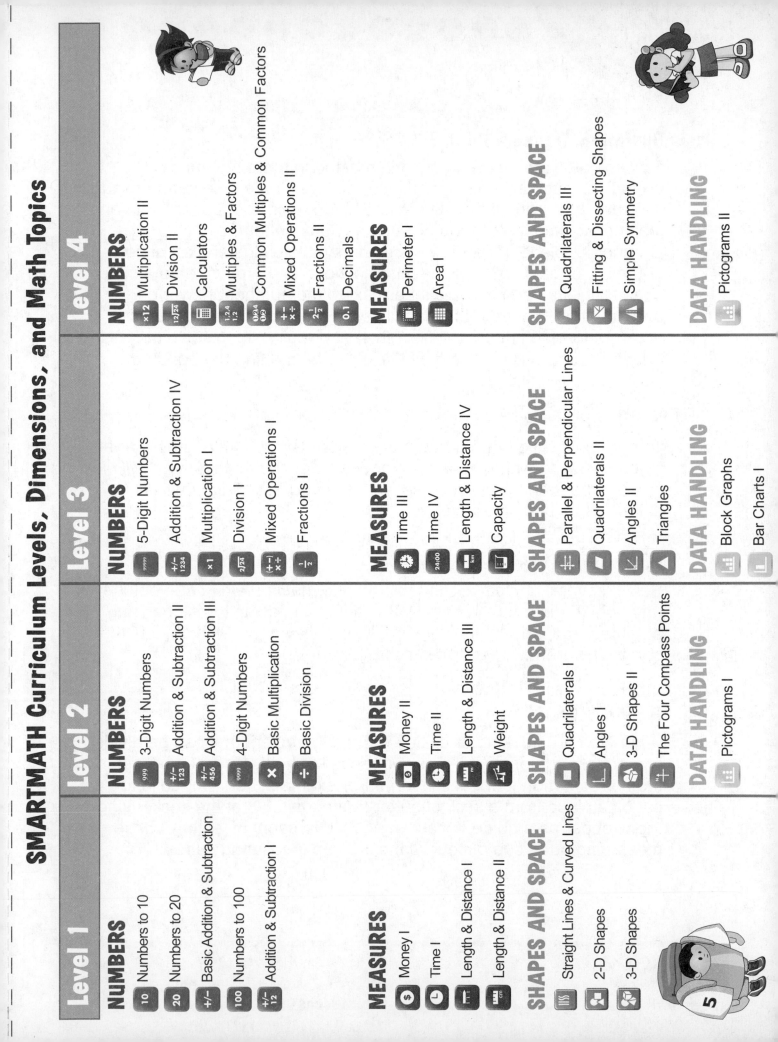

Operation: Treasure Hunt

To stimulate your child's interest in mastering more advanced operations such as dividing 3-digit numbers, create a secret message treasure hunt. Hide a small treat or toy. On a piece of paper, write an incomplete clue to its location, such as *Look under the* _____. On another piece of paper, write the incomplete clue and an unsolved equation for each letter of the missing word, or words. Create a code chart that lists each missing letter next to the number answer of one equation. Beneath the blank lines in the clue, write the number answers for each missing letter. Then ask your child to solve the equations in order to read the missing word and find the treasure.

24-Hour Time Talk

To help your child learn 24-hour time, start using 24-hour time format when speaking with him or her. For example, you might say, "*I will pick you up after band practice at sixteen hundred,*" or "*Breakfast will be served at zero, eight hundred.*"

Name That Angle

Select several objects around your house that contain acute, obtuse, and right angles. Play a game with your child, taking turns choosing an object and naming its types of angles. Play again with objects that contain different types of triangles.

Fractions Chef

When you are cooking or baking with an ingredient that can be divided into equal parts of a whole, ask your child to help you measure out the correct amount in fraction form. For example, ask your child to cut off a piece from a stick of butter that equals 3/8 of the stick, using the wrapper as a guide. Or ask your child to count by eighths while measuring out a cup of flour with a 1/8 cup measuring cup.

Numbers

| 99999 | +/− 1234 | ×1 | 2√24 |

3

LEVEL 3

This NUMBERS section introduces the concept of 5-digit numbers and offers practice with mathematical operations, including addition and subtraction, multiplication, and division.

5-DIGIT NUMBERS
- 4-Digit Numbers
- Count, Read, and Write 5-Digit Numbers
- Order 5-Digit Numbers
- 5-Digit Place Values
- 5-Digit Numbers: Word Problems

ADDITION AND SUBTRACTION IV
- Addition and Subtraction within Three Places
- Addition within Four Places
- Subtraction within Four Places
- Adding Three Numbers within Four Places
- Mixed Operations: Addition and Subtraction
- Commutative and Associative Properties of Addition
- 4-Digit Addition and Subtraction: Word Problems
- Estimate with 4-Digit Numbers

MULTIPLICATION I
- Multiply 1-Digit Numbers
- Multiply a 2-Digit Number by a 1-Digit Number
- Multiply a 3-Digit Number by a 1-Digit Number
- Multiplication Word Problems
- Estimate with Multiplication

DIVISION I
- Divide 1- and 2-Digit Numbers
- Learn Short Division
- Use Short Division
- Long Division with 1-Digit Divisors and 2-Digit Dividends
- 2-Digit Dividend Word Problems
- Long Division with 1-Digit Divisors and 3-Digit Dividends
- 3-Digit Dividend Word Problems
- Estimate with Division

5-Digit Numbers
LEVEL 3 NUMBERS

Learn It!

Ten Thousand is written as **10,000**. It comes after 9,999.

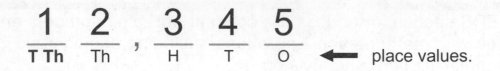

<u>1</u> <u>2</u> , <u>3</u> <u>4</u> <u>5</u> ← place values.
T Th Th   H   T   O

12,345 = **10,000** + 2,000 + 300 + 40 + 5

In word form, 12,345 is written as twelve thousand, three hundred forty-five.

A number that has exactly 5 place values is a **5-digit number**.

THOUSANDS	4 digits	9,997; 9,998; 9,999
TEN THOUSANDS	5 digits	10,000; 10,001;……99,999

Each extra place value makes a number 10 times larger.

100 is ten times bigger than 10.
100 = 10 x 10

1,000 is ten times bigger than 100.
1,000 = 10 x 100

10,000 is ten times bigger than 1,000.
10,000 = 10 x 1,000

Use It!

Look at the numbers in the box to answer the following questions.

27,987	97,627	25,472	5,013
15,473	19,101	96,628	

1. Which number is not a **5-digit number**? _____

2. Which number is the largest? _____

3. Which number comes right after 15,472? _____

4. Which number comes between 96,627 _____
   and 96,629?

....

1. 5,013 does not have a **ten-thousands** place.
   It is a 4-digit number, not a **5-digit number**.

2. 97,627 is the largest number in the box.

3. The next number after 15,472 is 15,473.

4. The number between 96,627 and 96,629 is 96,628.

Answer Ⓐ

Write each number in number form.

four thousand, seven hundred twenty-three

_____

thousands	hundreds	tens	ones
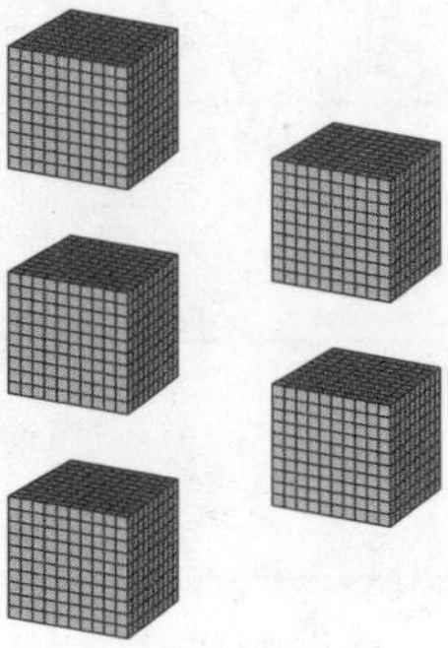	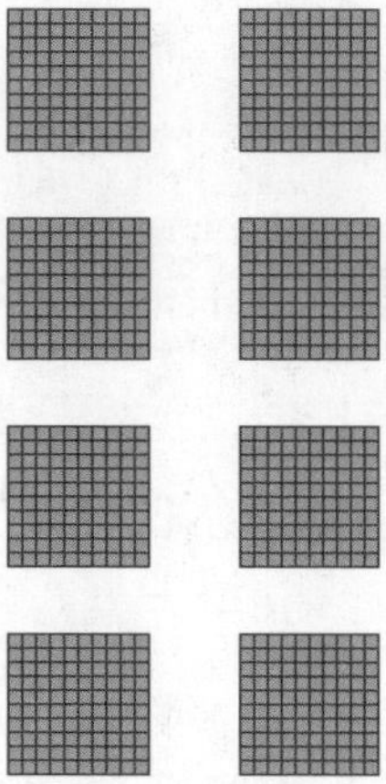		

_____

Write the number to complete each pattern.

8,907; 8,908; 8,909; _____ ; 8,911; 8,912

500; 1,000; _____ ; 2,000; 2,500; 3,000

9,000; 8,000; 7,000; 6,000; 5,000; _____

Write the **5-digit numbers**.

10,000	10,000		
20,000	20,000		
30,000	30,000		
40,000	40,000		
50,000	50,000		
60,000	60,000		
70,000	70,000		
80,000	80,000		
90,000	90,000		

Match each number with its word form.

10,000 •   • seventy thousand

20,000 •   • ten thousand

30,000 •   • eighty thousand

40,000 •   • fifty thousand

50,000 •   • thirty thousand

60,000 •   • twenty thousand

70,000 •   • ninety thousand

80,000 •   • forty thousand

90,000 •   • sixty thousand

Count, Read, and Write 5-Digit Numbers (iii)

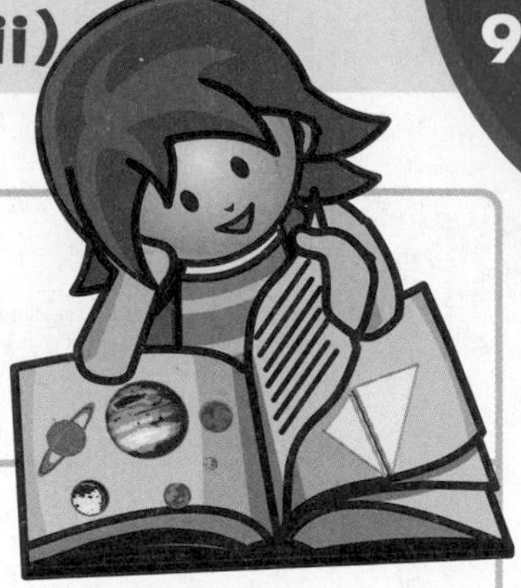

Write each number in word form.

67,982

____

____

45,203

____

____

79,115

____

____

34,822

____

____

19,676

____

____

Write each number in number form.

forty-five thousand, six hundred six   _____

seventy-two thousand, nine hundred
twenty-three   _____

thirteen thousand, eight hundred
forty-one   _____

sixty thousand, five hundred thirty-two   _____

ninety-nine thousand, four hundred
fifty-three   _____

Write the numbers from smallest to largest.

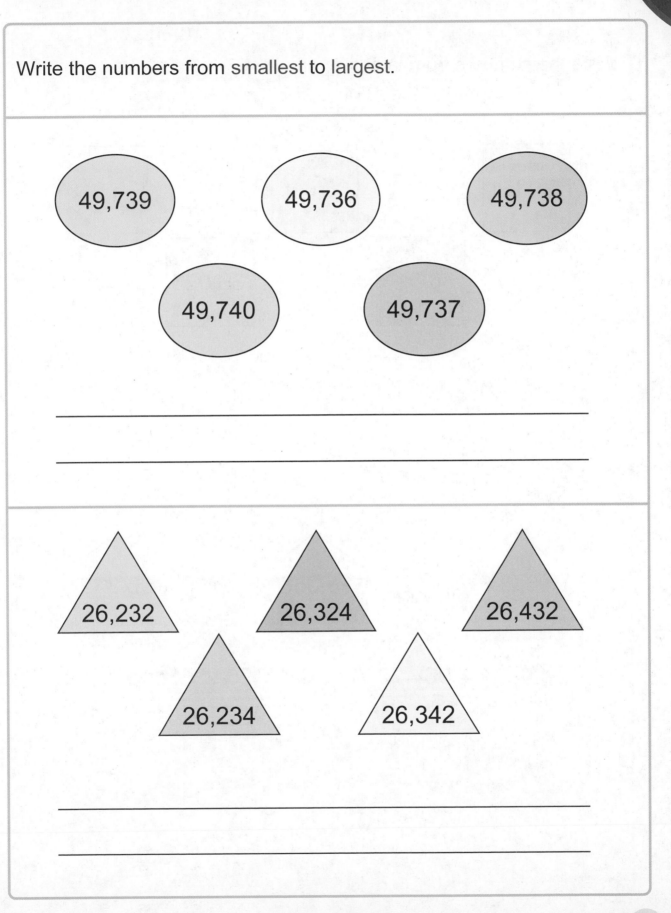

49,739   49,736   49,738

49,740   49,737

_____

_____

26,232   26,324   26,432

26,234   26,342

_____

_____

Write the numbers from largest to smallest.

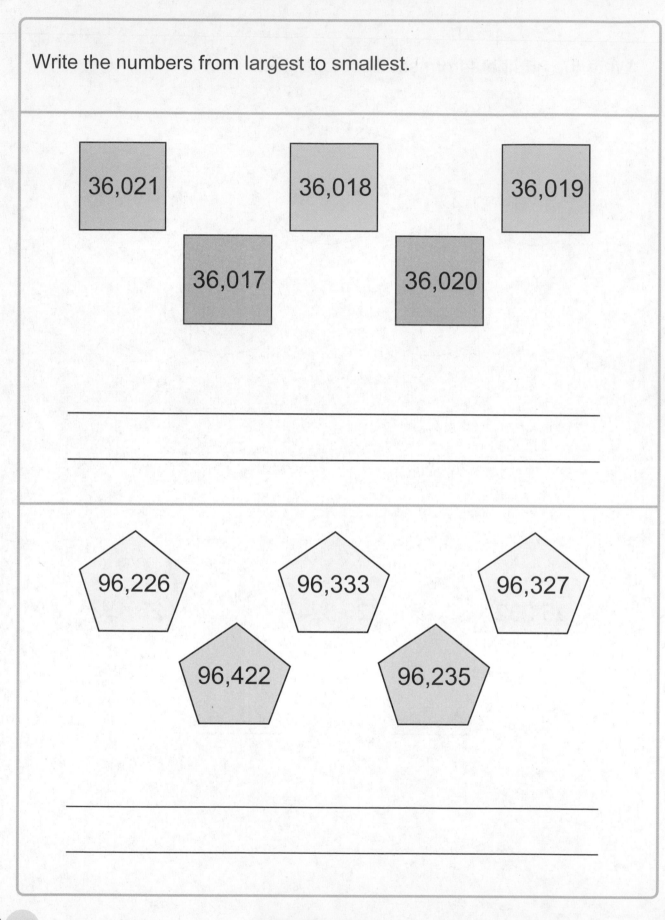

_____

_____

_____

_____

99999

Write the digit in the **ten thousands** place.

45,920 _____   29,189 _____

67,547 _____   89,316 _____

98,346 _____   59,010 _____

Write the place value of the underlined digit.

64,000   _____ place

59,738   _____ place

32,798   _____ place

14,921   _____ place

27,349   _____ place

78,466   _____ place

93,584   _____ place

63,919   _____ place

5-Digit Place Values (ii)

Complete each number sentence.

$86,344 = \underline{80,000} + 6,000 + \underline{} + 40 + \underline{}$

$\underline{} = 40,000 + 2,000 + 50 + 6$

$27,981 = 20,000 + \underline{} + 900 + \underline{} + 1$

$54,073 = \underline{} + 4,000 + \underline{} + 3$

Write what must be done to change each number on the left to the number at its right.

13,456 ➜ 18,456	Add _____ to the _____ place.
12,756 ➜ 32,756	Add _____ to the _____ place.
57,053 ➜ 57,853	Add _____ to the _____ place.

Write the numbers.

A number with a 3 in the ones place, a 7 in the tens place, a 0 in the hundreds place, a 9 in the thousands place, and a 1 in the ten thousands place.

_____

A number with a 2 in the ten thousands place, a 4 in the ones place, a 3 in the hundreds place, an 8 in the tens place, and a 6 in the thousands place.

_____

A number with a 4 in the hundreds place, a 2 in the tens place, a 7 in the ten thousands place, a 5 in the ones place, and a 9 in the thousands place.

_____

A number with a 5 in the tens place, a 4 in the hundreds place, an 8 in the ones place, a 3 in the ten thousands place, and a 1 in the thousands place.

_____

A number with a 0 in the thousands place, a 5 in the tens place, a 4 in the ten thousands place, a 1 in the ones place, and a 2 in the hundreds place.

_____

Mindy has $35,682 in her bank account. She wants to buy a car that costs $36,682. How much more money does Mindy need to buy the car?

_____

Jesse collects puzzle pieces. He has a total of 23,500 pieces. How many more puzzle pieces does he need to reach 25,500 puzzle pieces?

_____ pieces

Felicia and Robin are playing a video game. Felicia has 15,000 points and Robin has 20,000 points. If they combine their points, how many total points will they have?

_____ points

Justin and Jim have been collecting baseball cards for eleven years. Justin has a total of 12,000 baseball cards and Jim has a total of 16,000 baseball cards. How many baseball cards do they have in all?

_____ cards

Susie's parents bought a new boat. The boat cost $19,500. Susie knows that their old boat cost $14,500. How much more does the new boat cost than the old boat cost?

_____ more

Each shipment of toys to Tina's Toy Store contains 10,000 boxes. How many boxes do 3 shipments contain?

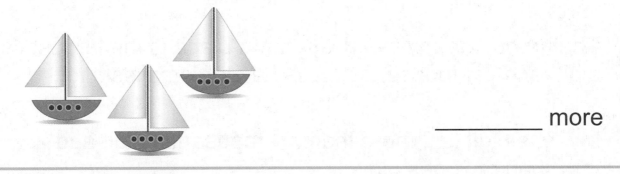

_____ boxes

Use the numbers in the bubble to solve the problem.

6   5   8   4   2

I am a **5-digit number** made up of 4 even-numbered digits and 1 odd-numbered digit.

The number in my **ten thousands** place is the largest digit, and my thousands place has the smallest digit.

My tens digit is 2 more than my thousands digit and 2 less than my ones digit.

My hundreds digit is the sum of the other 4 digits divided by 4.

What number am I?   _____

MELLOW — HYPER
GRUMPY — HAPPY
TOUGH — SWEET
CLUMSY — GRACEFUL
SHY — CONFIDENT

Mugo

sister:

pets:

Addition with 4-Digit Numbers

Learn It!

Here is how to add 4-digit numbers with regrouping.

Step 1: Add the ones.
Regroup if needed, carrying 10 ones to the tens place.

Step 2: Add the tens.
Regroup if needed, carrying 10 tens to the hundreds place.

Step 3: Add the hundreds.
Regroup if needed, carrying 10 hundreds to the thousands place.

Step 4: Add the thousands.

Example:

$$3277 + 1536 = ?$$

	1	1	
Th	H	T	O
3,	2	7	7
+ 1,	5	3	6
4,	8	1	3

Step 1: Ones place: 7 + 6 = 13.
Keep the 3 and carry the 10.

Step 2: Tens place: 10 + 70 + 30 = 110.
Keep the 10 and carry the 100.

Step 3: Hundreds place: 100 + 200 + 500 = 800

Step 4: Thousands place: 3,000 + 1,000 = 4,000

Commutative Property of Addition: Numbers can
be added in any order.
3000 + 1000 = 1000 + 3000

Associative Property of Addition: Numbers that
are added can be grouped in any order.
(100 + 200) + 500 = 100 + (200 + 500)

Learn It!

Here is how to subtract 4-digit numbers with regrouping.

Step 1: Subtract the ones. Regroup if needed, borrowing 10 ones from the tens place.

Step 2: Subtract the tens. Regroup if needed, borrowing 10 tens from the hundreds place.

Step 3: Subtract the hundreds. Regroup if needed, borrowing 10 hundreds from the thousands place.

Step 4: Subtract the thousands.

Example:

$2521 - 1532 = ?$

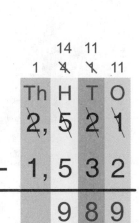

Step 1: Ones place: Regroup, borrowing 10 ones from the tens place.
$11 - 2 = 9$

Step 2: Tens place: Regroup, borrowing 10 tens from the hundreds place.
11 tens – 3 tens = 8 tens

Step 3: Hundreds place: Regroup, borrowing 10 hundreds from the thousands place.
14 hundreds – 5 hundreds = 9 hundreds

Step 4: Thousands place:
1 thousand – 1 thousand = 0 thousands

Use It!

Example 1

Add.

$$\begin{array}{r} 2\ 5\ 9\ 3 \\ +\ 1\ 7\ 4\ 8 \\ \hline \end{array}$$

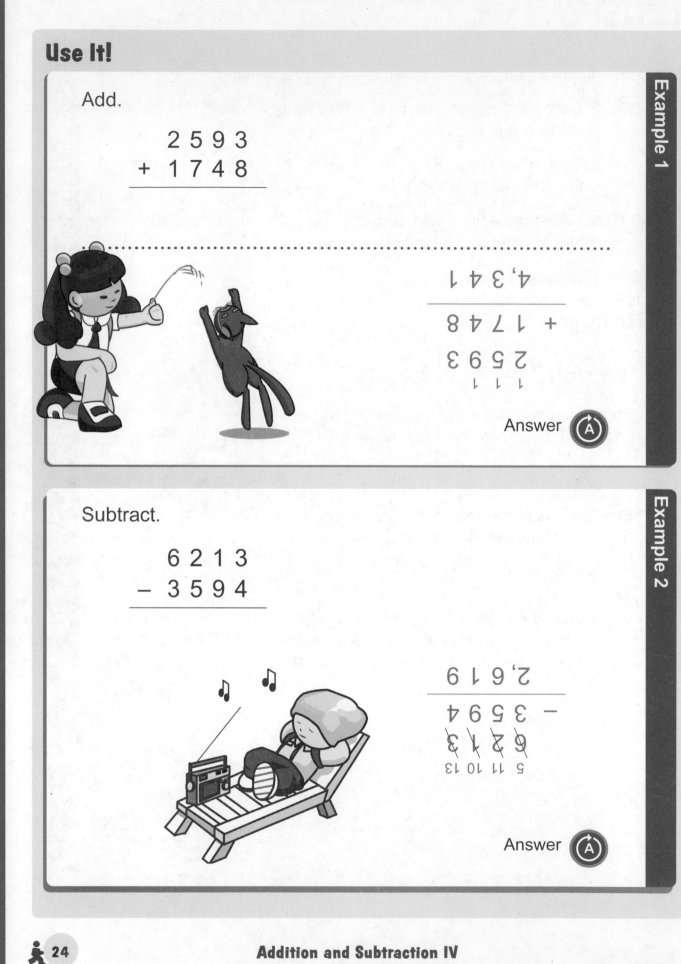

Answer Ⓐ

$$\begin{array}{r} \overset{1\ 1\ 1}{2\ 5\ 9\ 3} \\ +\ 1\ 7\ 4\ 8 \\ \hline 4,3\ 4\ 1 \end{array}$$

Example 2

Subtract.

$$\begin{array}{r} 6\ 2\ 1\ 3 \\ -\ 3\ 5\ 9\ 4 \\ \hline \end{array}$$

Answer Ⓐ

$$\begin{array}{r} \overset{5\ 11\ 10\ 13}{6\ 2\ 1\ 3} \\ -\ 3\ 5\ 9\ 4 \\ \hline 2,6\ 1\ 9 \end{array}$$

Solve.

```
    2 5 0          4 5 3          2 4 8
  +   1 7        + 4 5 6        + 3 1 7
  _____      _____      _____


    4 7 9          5 9 4          6 0 6
  − 3 5 6        −   3 8        − 2 4 1
  _____      _____      _____
```

Jerry's pet store has 401 goldfish. Charlie's pet store has 263 more goldfish than Jerry's. Adrian's pet store has 318 fewer goldfish than Charlie's. How many goldfish does Adrian's pet store have?

_____

Add.

```
   3 2 5 0          2 6 3 1          3 0 4 7
 +   3 4 6        + 5 3 5 2        + 5 8 1 1
 ─────────        ─────────        ─────────


   5 1 8 2          7 0 3 9          1 5 6 6
 + 3 6 7 5        + 1 9 2 3        + 4 6 2 3
 ─────────        ─────────        ─────────


   3 5 1 0          4 9 5 3          2 3 5 1
 +   1 9 9        + 1 4 2 7        + 6 6 5 2
 ─────────        ─────────        ─────────


   3 6 8 9          1 6 8 5          3 9 6 4
 +   9 1 1        + 6 6 7 9        + 1 0 9 8
 ─────────        ─────────        ─────────
```

Subtract.

$$\begin{array}{r} 3260 \\ -230 \\ \hline \end{array} \qquad \begin{array}{r} 9152 \\ -2041 \\ \hline \end{array} \qquad \begin{array}{r} 4856 \\ -2314 \\ \hline \end{array}$$

$$\begin{array}{r} 1627 \\ -903 \\ \hline \end{array} \qquad \begin{array}{r} 7787 \\ -3729 \\ \hline \end{array} \qquad \begin{array}{r} 3516 \\ -2054 \\ \hline \end{array}$$

$$\begin{array}{r} 1460 \\ -1172 \\ \hline \end{array} \qquad \begin{array}{r} 3798 \\ -1809 \\ \hline \end{array} \qquad \begin{array}{r} 5138 \\ -3247 \\ \hline \end{array}$$

$$\begin{array}{r} 2000 \\ -747 \\ \hline \end{array} \qquad \begin{array}{r} 4860 \\ -2895 \\ \hline \end{array} \qquad \begin{array}{r} 2673 \\ -1986 \\ \hline \end{array}$$

Adding Three Numbers within Four Places

Add.

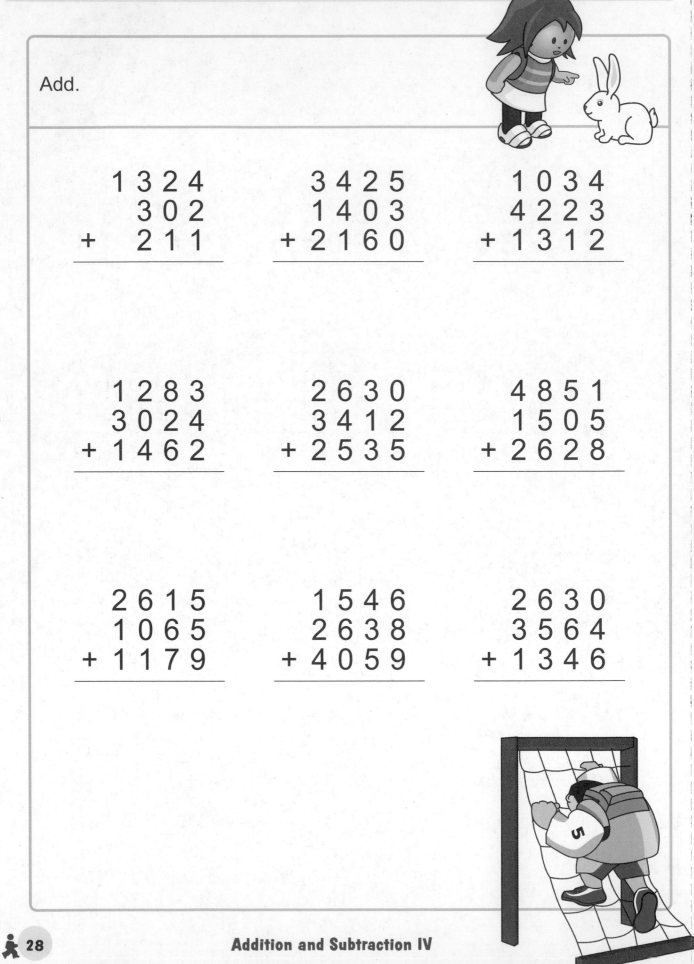

```
    1 3 2 4        3 4 2 5        1 0 3 4
      3 0 2        1 4 0 3        4 2 2 3
  +   2 1 1      + 2 1 6 0      + 1 3 1 2
  _____      _____      _____
```

```
    1 2 8 3        2 6 3 0        4 8 5 1
    3 0 2 4        3 4 1 2        1 5 0 5
  + 1 4 6 2      + 2 5 3 5      + 2 6 2 8
  _____      _____      _____
```

```
    2 6 1 5        1 5 4 6        2 6 3 0
    1 0 6 5        2 6 3 8        3 5 6 4
  + 1 1 7 9      + 4 0 5 9      + 1 3 4 6
  _____      _____      _____
```

Addition and Subtraction IV

Mixed Operations: Addition and Subtraction

Solve from left to right.

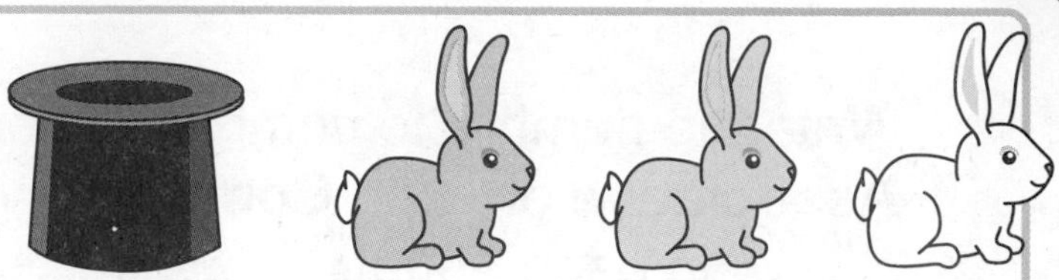

1397 + 2401 – 3294 = ________

5835 – 1729 + 2743 = ________

2517 + 1945 – 3051 = ________

2642 + 3695 – 4870 = ________

4286 – 2977 + 1708 = ________

5000 – 2306 + 4123 = ________

3658 + 4796 – 2999 = ________

1692 + 3368 – 5060 = ________

1926 – 1347 + 3175 = ________

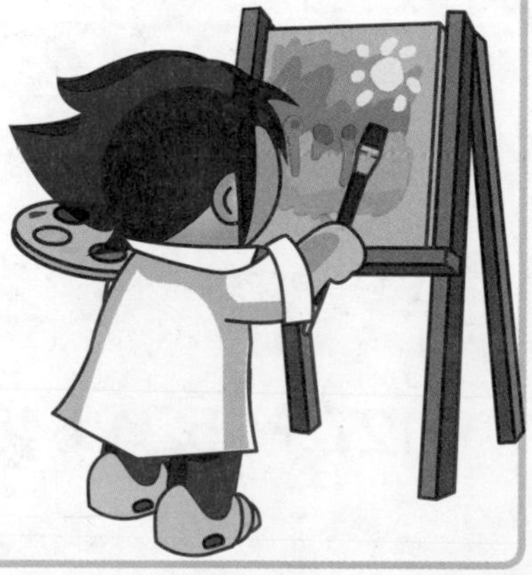

Write the number to complete each equation. Then, write **A** for **Associative** or **C** for **Commutative** in the box to name the property shown in each equation.

692 + (258 + 951) = (692 + _____) + 951 □

(198 + 501) + 538 = 198 + (501 + _____) □

3089 + 2641 = 2641 + _____ □

3725 + 2864 = _____ + 3725 □

Compare the two statements. If they are equal, write **=**.
If they are not equal, write **≠**.

742 − (315 + 139) _____ 742 − (139 + 315)

228 + (231 + 108) _____ 228 + (231 − 108)

187 + 264 + 315 _____ 264 + 187 + 315

(428 − 196) + 119 _____ 119 + (428 − 196)

127 + 352 + 648 + 258 _____ 127 + (352 + 648) + 258

Rearrange the sequence of addition to simplify each calculation.

205 + 172 + 428

= 205 + (172 + _____)

= _____ + _____

= _____

345 + 216 + 654

= (345 + _____) + 216

= _____ + _____

= _____

178 + 209 + 1220 + 199

= (_____ + _____) + (_____ + _____)

= _____ + _____

= _____

Solve.

Nancy's News Stand sold 2,847 magazines during the winter and 1,360 magazines during the summer. How many more magazines were sold during the winter?

_____ magazines

It usually takes Sam's mother 8,036 seconds to drive to the airport, but yesterday it took her 9,463 seconds. How much longer did the drive to the airport take yesterday?

_____ seconds

Perry's class counted the fruits in a supermarket. There were 1,788 apples and 3,128 oranges. 258 of the apples were yellow. How many more oranges were there than apples?

_____ oranges

Solve.

Bella's Bakery sold 2,012 doughnuts last year. This year, it sold 1,508 more doughnuts. How many doughnuts did the bakery sell this year in all?

_____ doughnuts

On a farm, there are 1,866 ducks and 1,395 pigs. 409 of the pigs are brown. How many animals are there in all?

_____ animals

Jim spent 2,883 seconds working on a computer project, and another 3,198 seconds playing a computer game. How long did Jim use the computer?

_____ seconds

Estimate with 4-Digit Numbers (i)

First, round off the numbers to the nearest 1,000. Then, estimate the sum or difference.

4026 – 1985 = ?

3,000 5,000 4,000 1,000 2,000

9311 – 4121 = ?

7,000 6,000 5,000 4,000 3,000

3990 – 2006 = ?

1,000 2,000 3,000 4,000 5,000

3895 + 2006 = ?

5,000 3,000 2,000 7,000 6,000

5497 + 2689 = ?

7,000 9,000 6,000 3,000 8,000

3926 + 2975 = ?

6,000 4,000 7,000 8,000 1,000

Round each number to the nearest hundred. Then, draw a ✔ in the box next to the correct answer for each problem.

Jeff has been shopping for a professional camera kit that costs about $2,500. Which one of these camera kits is closest to the total that he wants to spend?

Camera: $2,200   Flash: $190   Lens: $410   ☐

Camera: $1,750   Flash: $500   Lens: $400   ☐

Camera: $1,600   Flash: $270   Lens: $260   ☐

Camera: $1,600   Flash: $680   Lens: $500   ☐

Adrienne wants to buy a laptop and a printer. Which one of these packages should she choose if she only wants to spend about $2,100?

Laptop: $2,000   Printer: $265   ☐

Laptop: $1,800   Printer: $460   ☐

Laptop: $1,650   Printer: $450   ☐

Laptop: $1,700   Printer: $550   ☐

Laptop: $1,580   Printer: $429   ☐

Star Question

Solve.

Mr. Stockton took $2,000 out of the bank and bought two electric appliances. The sum of the prices was above $1,500. How much money did he have left after buying the appliances?

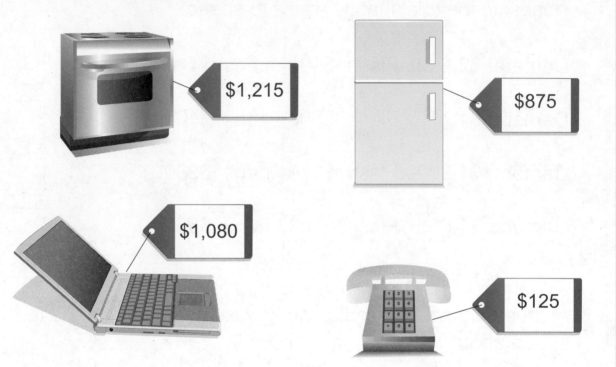

$1,215

$875

$1,080

$125

(Hint: Use estimation to eliminate the combinations of items that would cost less than $1,500 or more than $2,000)

_____

Addition and Subtraction IV

Multiplication I
LEVEL 3 NUMBERS

Learn It!

Here is how to multiply with regrouping.

Multiply 564 by 3.

$$\begin{array}{r} 5\ 6\ 4 \\ \times \qquad 3 \\ \hline \end{array}$$

Step 1: First, multiply the ones digit of the top number by the bottom number:

4 x 3 = 12
Keep the 2.
Carry the 1.

$$\begin{array}{r} 1 \\ 5\ 6\ 4 \\ \times \qquad 3 \\ \hline 2 \end{array}$$

Step 2: Next, multiply the tens digit of the top number by the bottom number and add the carried number:

6 x 3 = 18
18 + 1 = 19
Keep the 9.
Carry the 1.

$$\begin{array}{r} 1\ 1 \\ 5\ 6\ 4 \\ \times \qquad 3 \\ \hline 9\ 2 \end{array}$$

Step 3: Then, multiply the hundreds digit of the top number by the bottom number and add the carried number.

5 x 3 = 15
15 + 1 = 16
Keep the 6.
Carry the 1.

$$\begin{array}{r} 1\ 1\ 1 \\ 5\ 6\ 4 \\ \times \qquad 3 \\ \hline 1,\ 6\ 9\ 2 \end{array}$$

Step 4: Add the thousand.
The answer is 1,692.

Multiplication I

Use It!

A box weighs 367 grams. How much do 4 boxes weigh?

_____

Answer (A)

Set up the problem in column form.

```
  3 6 7
x     4
_____
```

Step 1: First, multiply 7 by 4.
$7 \times 4 = 28$
Keep the 8.
Carry the 2.

```
    2
  3 6 7
x     4
_____
      8
```

Step 2: Next, multiply 6 by 4 and add 2.
$6 \times 4 = 24$
$24 + 2 = 26$
Keep the 6.
Carry the 2.

```
    2 2
  3 6 7
x     4
_____
    6 8
```

Step 3: Then, multiply 3 by 4 and add 2.
$3 \times 4 = 12$
$12 + 2 = 14$
Keep the 4.
Carry the 1.

Step 4: Add the thousand.
The answer is 1,428.
4 boxes weigh 1,428 grams.

```
    1 2 2
    3 6 7
x       4
_____
  1,4 6 8
```

Multiply 1-Digit Numbers

Multiply.

$$\begin{array}{r} 6 \\ \times\ 7 \\ \hline \end{array}$$ $$\begin{array}{r} 5 \\ \times\ 4 \\ \hline \end{array}$$ $$\begin{array}{r} 3 \\ \times\ 8 \\ \hline \end{array}$$ $$\begin{array}{r} 7 \\ \times\ 5 \\ \hline \end{array}$$ $$\begin{array}{r} 9 \\ \times\ 6 \\ \hline \end{array}$$

Write an equation to match each picture.

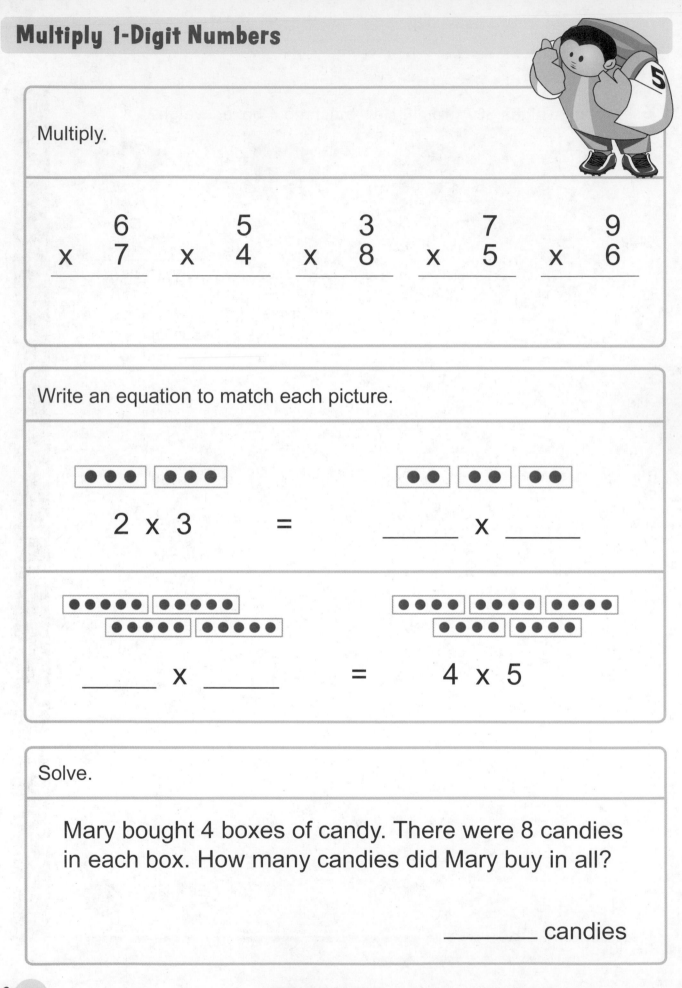

2 x 3   =   _____ x _____

_____ x _____   =   4 x 5

Solve.

Mary bought 4 boxes of candy. There were 8 candies in each box. How many candies did Mary buy in all?

_____ candies

Multiply.

```
      12          18          16
  x    1      x    1      x    1
```

```
      28          10          10
  x    0      x    3      x    5
```

```
      10          10          42          23
  x    6      x    7      x    5      x    7
```

```
      35          62          17          14
  x    3      x    2      x    4      x    8
```

Multiply.

```
    12          23          18          26
x    6      x    5      x    9      x    7
```

```
    33          46          15          18
x    7      x    3      x    6      x    3
```

```
    54          72          64          47
x    2      x    3      x    6      x    3
```

```
    54          62          23
x    5      x    3      x    6
```

Multiply.

How many apples are there in 9 bowls?

_____ apples

How many doughnuts are there in 5 boxes?

_____ doughnuts

How many bananas are there in 17 bunches?

_____ bananas

How many candies are there in 16 bags?

_____ candies

Multiply.

```
    400          200
x     2       x    2
```

```
    400          237          158          456
x     3       x    2       x    4       x    3
```

```
    372          512          326          159
x     2       x    4       x    5       x    6
```

```
    123          251          397          403
x     7       x    6       x    5       x    7
```

Multiply.

```
    5 3 2        3 2 6        2 7 8        3 4 7
  x     6      x     4      x     7      x     5
```

```
    6 9 2        7 0 8        8 1 2        9 7 3
  x     4      x     6      x     3      x     2
```

```
    4 5 6        6 4 1        5 2 3        6 9 1
  x     5      x     7      x     4      x     7
```

```
    8 0 7        4 6 7
  x     3      x     8
```

Multiply to solve each word problem.

Jason is 18 years old. His Uncle Johnny is three times as old as Jason. How old is Uncle Johnny?

Jason   Uncle Johnny

_____

There are 11 players on a soccer team. How many players are on 7 soccer teams?

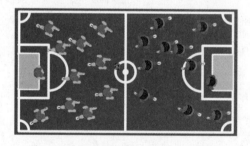

_____

A huge pool is 200 meters long. Joanna swam 3 laps in the pool. How many meters did Joanna swim?

_____

Multiply to solve each word problem.

Ronald runs 425 meters three times every day. What is the total number of meters Ronald runs each day?

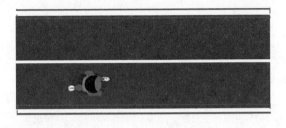

_____

Jerry has 4 times as many baseball cards as Al. Al has 132 baseball cards. How many baseball cards does Jerry have?

_____

Mr. Marco went to a sporting goods store. If he bought 5 baseball mitts that cost $126 each, how much did he spend in all?

$126

_____

Estimate with Multiplication

Round the larger number to the nearest 10. Then, multiply to estimate the answer.

36 x 2 = approximately _____40 X 2 = 80_____

24 x 6 = approximately _____

7 x 42 = approximately _____

49 x 5 = approximately _____

234 x 7 = approximately _____

8 x 397 = approximately _____

165 x 4 = approximately _____

451 x 9 = approximately _____

Estimate Word Problems

Round the larger number to the nearest 10 to solve each word problem.

Every day, Maria spends $5 at the deli on lunch. Approximately how much money does Maria spend on lunch in 22 days?

DELI LUNCH $5

about _____

Allister's mom bought bags of popcorn for the 2nd grade sleepover party. Each bag cost $2. Approximately how much money did she spend if she bought 192 bags of popcorn?

$2

about _____

Star Question

Solve.

The junior baseball team of Brockport started a fundraiser selling caps, t-shirts, and candy bars. The team went to two locations: Boston and Amherst.

In Boston, they sold 102 caps, 246 t-shirts, and 537 candy bars.

In Amherst, they sold 78 caps, 194 t-shirts, and 673 candy bars.

Caps cost $5, t-shirts cost $8, and candy bars cost $2.

How much money did they raise?

selling caps: _____

selling t-shirts: _____

selling candy bars: _____

in all: _____

MELLOW ──○○○●○── HYPER
GRUMPY ──○○○○●── HAPPY
TOUGH ──○○○○●── SWEET
CLUMSY ──●○○○○── GRACEFUL
SHY ──○○○●○── CONFIDENT

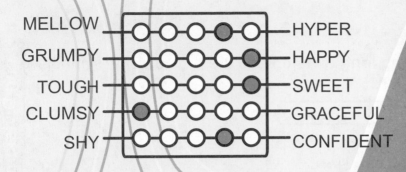

BONITA

PETS:

Learn It!

Here is how to divide using **long division** and the $\overline{\smash{)}}$ division symbol.

$$374 \div 3 = ?$$

Step 1: Divide the hundreds.

```
      1
  3 ) 3 7 4
      3
```
$3 \times 1 = 3$

Step 2: Divide the tens.

```
      1 2
  3 ) 3 7 4
      3
      7
      6
      1
```
$3 \times 2 = 6$
$7 - 6 = 1$

Step 3: Divide the ones.

```
      1 2 4
  3 ) 3 7 4
      3
      7
      6
      1 4
      1 2
          2
```
$3 \times 4 = 12$
$14 - 12 = 2$

This is the remainder. → 2

Therefore, $374 \div 3 = 124$ with 2 left over. The answer is 124 r 2.

In **long division**, an equation is written out in steps.

In **short division**, an equation is mostly solved by mental math.

Use It!

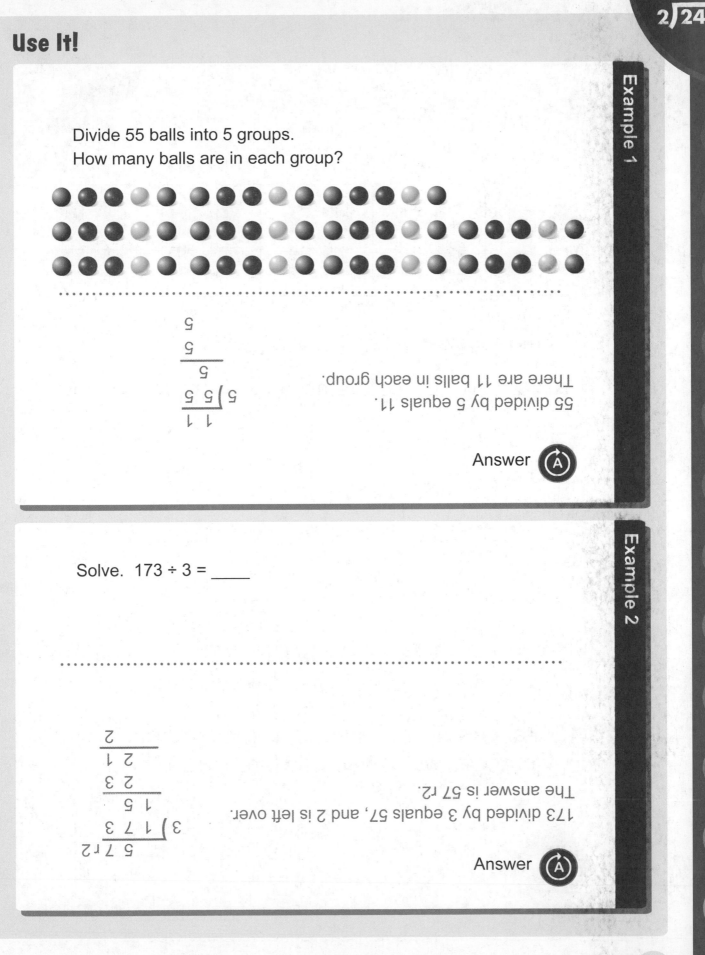

Example 1

Divide 55 balls into 5 groups.
How many balls are in each group?

Answer Ⓐ

55 divided by 5 equals 11.
There are 11 balls in each group.

$$
\begin{array}{r}
11 \\
5\,\overline{)\,55} \\
5 \\
\hline
5 \\
5 \\
\hline
\end{array}
$$

Example 2

Solve. 173 ÷ 3 = _____

Answer Ⓐ

173 divided by 3 equals 57, and 2 is left over.
The answer is 57 r2.

$$
\begin{array}{r}
57\ r2 \\
3\,\overline{)\,173} \\
15 \\
\hline
23 \\
21 \\
\hline
2 \\
\end{array}
$$

Divide 1- and 2-Digit Numbers

Divide.

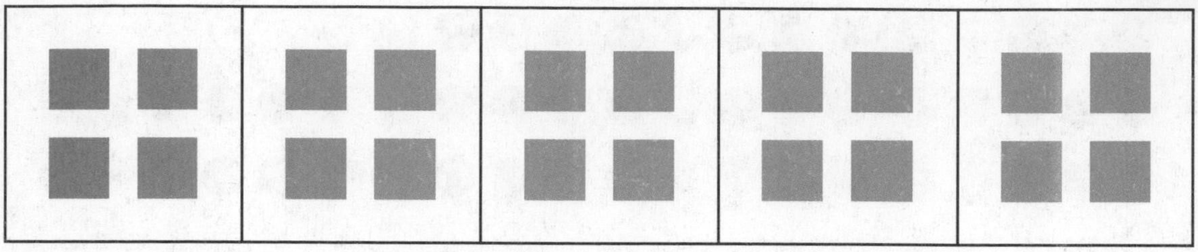

20 squares are divided into 5 equal groups.

There are _____ squares in each group.

$4 \div 2 =$ _____ $24 \div 3 =$ _____

$36 \div 6 =$ _____ $63 \div 7 =$ _____

$13 \div 2$ The remainder is _____.

$29 \div 6$ The remainder is _____.

If 18 oranges were shared among 6 children, how many oranges would each child receive?

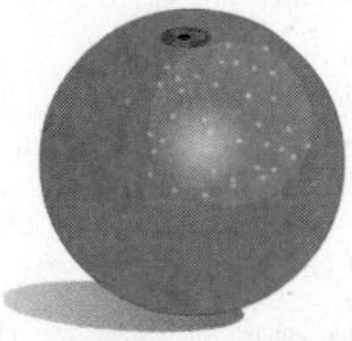

_____ oranges

Learn Short Division

Follow the steps to use **short division** to solve the question.

62 ÷ 5 = ?

Step 1:

□

5) 6 ₁ 2

Think: 6 ÷ 5 is about 1.

Write a 1 in the tens place of the answer area.

1 times 5 is 5. 6 minus 5 is 1.

Write a 1 to the left of the 2.

Think: 12 ÷ 5 is about 2.

Step 2:

1 □ r □

5) 6 ₁ 2

Write a 2 in the ones place of the answer area.

2 times 5 is 10. 12 minus 10 is 2.

Then, write the remainder.

Therefore,

62 ÷ 5 = _____

Use Short Division (i)

Use **short division** to solve each equation.

$3\overline{)15}$

Which number multiplied by 3 equals 15?

$3\overline{)49}$

Step 1

$3\overline{)49}$ → **Step 2** $3\overline{)49}$

$5\overline{)70}$

Step 1

$5\overline{)70}$ → **Step 2** $5\overline{)70}$

$6\overline{)95}$

Step 1

$6\overline{)95}$ → **Step 2** $6\overline{)95}$

Use Short Division (ii)

Use **short division** to solve each equation. Then, circle Mike's presents. The holiday presents whose equations have answers with a remainder of 1 belong to Mike.

$5 \overline{)59}$

$4 \overline{)81}$

$3 \overline{)54}$

$2 \overline{)18}$

$4 \overline{)67}$

$3 \overline{)76}$

Use **long division** to solve each equation.

$2\overline{)56}$ $\qquad$ $5\overline{)89}$ $\qquad$ $6\overline{)36}$

$9\overline{)97}$ $\qquad$ $7\overline{)98}$ $\qquad$ $3\overline{)56}$

$4\overline{)78}$ $\qquad$ $8\overline{)92}$

A space shuttle under alien attack wants to escape to a safe planet. At the top of each planet, there is a division equation. The equation whose answer includes no remainder is safe. Use **long division** to solve each equation, then circle the safe planet.

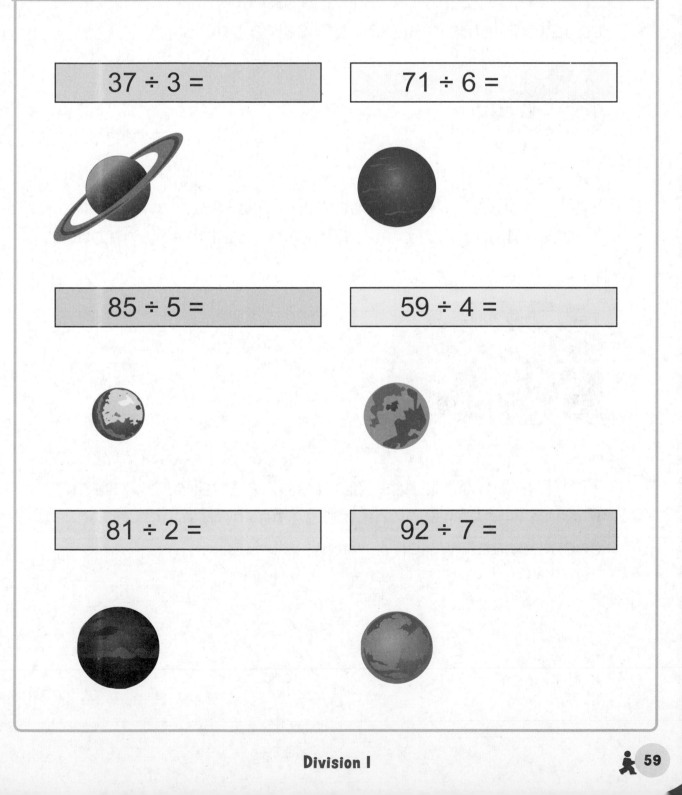

$$37 \div 3 =$$

$$71 \div 6 =$$

$$85 \div 5 =$$

$$59 \div 4 =$$

$$81 \div 2 =$$

$$92 \div 7 =$$

Divide to solve each word problem.

Bill wants to spend $45 on 3 pairs of sneakers for his children. How much will he spend on each pair of sneakers if they all cost the same price?

_____

Pedro spent $78 on 6 computer games. How much did he spend on each game if they all cost the same price?

_____

There are 5 bananas that weigh a total of 55 grams. If each banana weighs the same, how much does each banana weigh?

_____ grams

Divide to solve each word problem.

Frank gave 84 marbles to his friends. If each friend received 7 marbles, how many friends got marbles?

_____ friends

A bag of oranges costs $4. Wilson has $51. How many bags of oranges can he buy?

_____ bags

Tim used 96 ft of ribbon to wrap his Christmas presents. If he used 8 ft of ribbon on each present, how many presents did he wrap with ribbon?

_____ presents

Use **long division** to solve each equation.

$2 \overline{)402}$ $9 \overline{)396}$ $4 \overline{)228}$

$3 \overline{)465}$ $8 \overline{)170}$ $5 \overline{)123}$

$7 \overline{)289}$ $4 \overline{)307}$

Write one number from the number bank to correctly complete each equation.

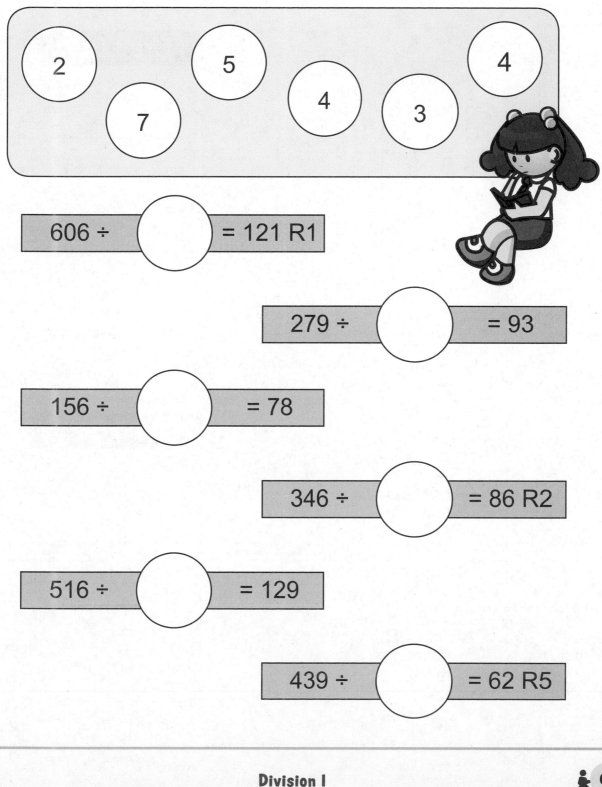

2   5   4

7   4   3

606 ÷ ◯ = 121 R1

279 ÷ ◯ = 93

156 ÷ ◯ = 78

346 ÷ ◯ = 86 R2

516 ÷ ◯ = 129

439 ÷ ◯ = 62 R5

Draw a ✔ in the box if the calculation is correct. Draw a ✗ if it is incorrect, then correctly solve the equation in the draft box on the right.

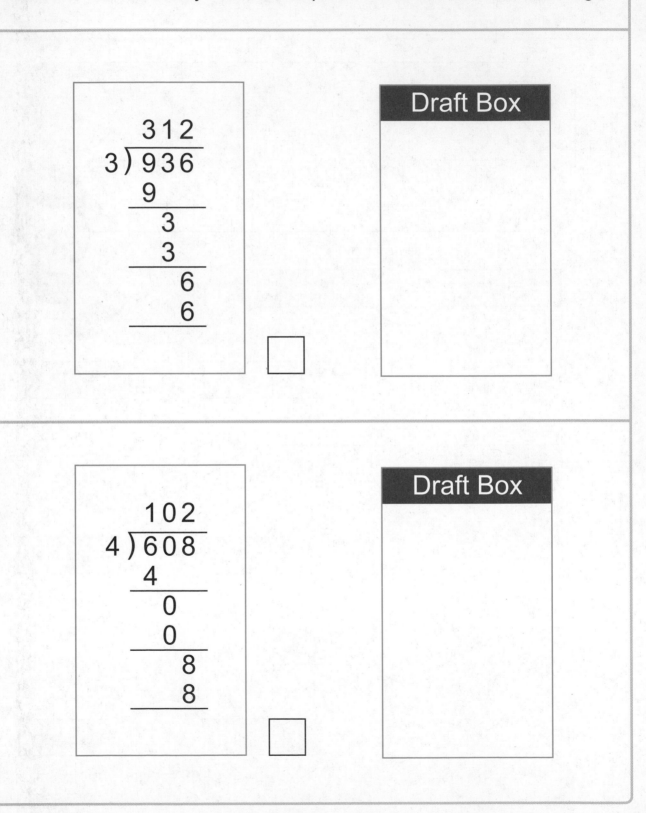

Draft Box

```
    312
3 ) 9 3 6
    9
    3
    3
      6
      6
```

Draft Box

```
    102
4 ) 6 0 8
    4
    0
    0
      8
      8
```

Divide to solve each word problem.

Julia has 156 straws. She needs 3 straws to make one triangle. How many triangles can she make?

_____ triangles

Mrs. Long spent $342 on 6 identical shirts. How much did she spend on each shirt?

_____

Mr. Jordan has $117. He wants to buy potted cactuses. How many can he buy, if each potted cactus costs $9?

_____ potted cactuses

3-Digit Dividend Word Problems (ii)

Divide to solve each word problem.

If 133 sweets are shared equally among 4 children, how many sweets will each child receive?

_____ sweets

9 tokens can be exchanged for a toy clown. Richard has 114 tokens. How many toy clowns can he get?

_____ toy clowns

Connie wants to buy a drum that costs $230. She can save $5 a day. How many days does she have to save in order to buy the drum?

_____ days

Division I

Estimate with Division

24

Solve.

Estimate 49 ÷ 8.   about _____

Estimate 48 ÷ 7.   about _____

Estimate 69 ÷ 4.   about _____

Estimate 85 ÷ 6.   about _____

Estimate 52 ÷ 3.   about _____

Estimate 71 ÷ 4.   about _____

Estimate 103 ÷ 8.   about _____

Estimate 233 ÷ 9.   about _____

Solve.

26 cookies are divided among 9 children. Estimate about how many cookies each child has received.

about _____ cookies

76 chocolates are divided among 5 boxes. Estimate about how many chocolates are in each box.

about _____ chocolates

61 cans of tuna fish are divided among 3 cats. Estimate about how many cans of tuna fish there will be for each cat.

about _____ cans

Solve.

36 slices of pizza are being divided among 7 children. Estimate about how many slices of pizza each child will receive.

about _____ slices

55 apples have been divided among 4 teachers. Estimate about how many apples each teacher has.

about _____ apples

109 books were divided among 6 teachers. Estimate about how many books each teacher has.

about _____ books

Solve.

Tommy wants to buy a scooter which costs $105.
He can save $8 a day. If he starts saving on July 3rd,
on which day will he have enough to buy a scooter?

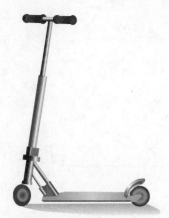

July _____

JULY

Sunday	Monday	Tuesday	Wednesday	Thursday	Friday	Saturday
1	2	3	4	5	6	7
8	9	10	11	12	13	14
15	16	17	18	19	20	21
22	23	24	25	26	27	28
29	30	31				

Star Questions (cont'd)

Solve.

A bakery wants to offer a special on a snack pack that contains 1 carton of milk, 2 cupcakes, and 3 doughnuts. There are 16 cartons of milk, 25 cupcakes and 41 doughnuts available for the special. How many snack packs can be prepared? How many of each item will be left over?

_____ snack packs

_____ milk carton(s) left over

_____ cupcake(s) left over

_____ doughnut(s) left over

Division I

MELLOW ●○○○● HYPER
GRUMPY ●○○○○ HAPPY
TOUGH ●○○○○ SWEET
CLUMSY ○●○○○ GRACEFUL
SHY ○○○○● CONFIDENT

Kay

PETS:

Directions: Cut out the number and symbol mini-cards along the dotted lines. Use the cards to build your own addition, subtraction, multiplication, or division equations. Try the idea below, and the ideas on the next few pages, too.

Short Division Speed Game with the mini-cards:

Get a partner and play a game to see who can solve short division equations the fastest using mental math. Use the $\overline{)}$ symbol mini-cards shown on this side as well as the number mini-cards.

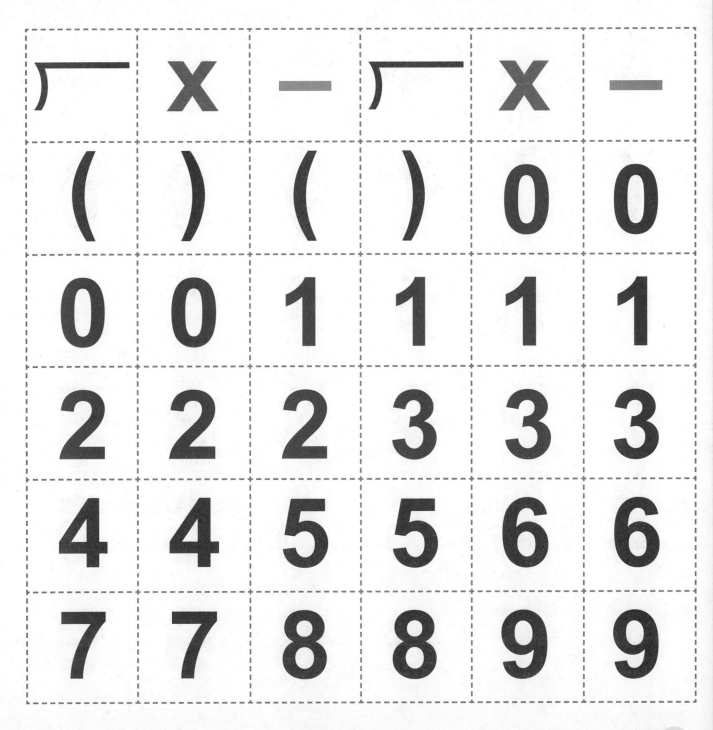

Numbers Tools – Number and Symbol Mini-Cards

More Ideas:

Use the number cards to make 3,4, and 5-digit numbers (place 3, 4, or 5 single-numbered cards next to each other, such as 642). Then, choose an equation symbol and a second number. Solve your equation. Use scrap paper to work out the equation if you need to.

Equation Race: Find a friend and have each player create an equation. Switch places and see who can solve the other player's equation first.

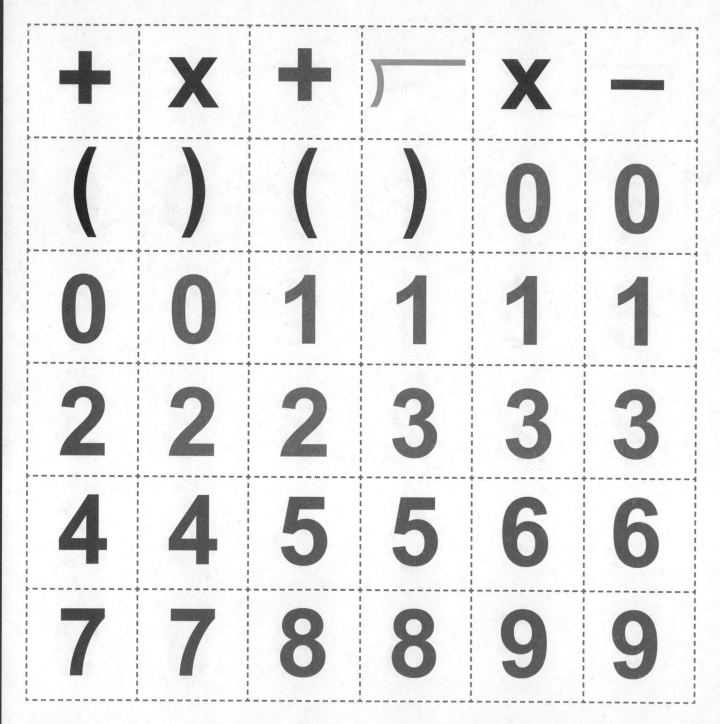

Number Tools

+/−
123

More Ideas: Build a few of your own 4-digit numbers with the number cards. Then, see if you can place them in order from largest to smallest, or smallest to largest. Try this with 3 and 5-digit numbers, too. Can you tell if each number is odd or even? Pick one of your numbers and answer the following: which number is in the tens place? If you were to round your number to the nearest hundred, what number would you get?

Make your own number patterns and sequences. For example, you might make a pattern that looks like this: 20 40 60 80 100..... See if a friend or family member can guess the pattern (+20).

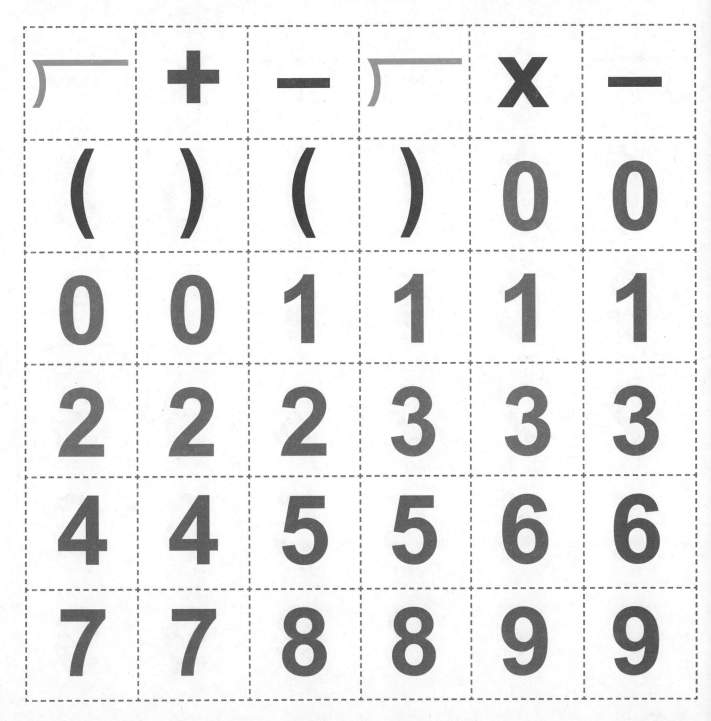

Numbers Tools – Number and Symbol Mini-Cards

More Ideas:

Make up your own multiplication and division equations. Find pictures of food, objects, or use real props to create word problem equations, then use the mini cards to show your answer. For example, you might use raisins to create and solve the following word problem: There are 33 raisins in the box and three friends want to share the raisins equally. How many raisins would each friend get? Place two cards with the number 1 next to each other to show the answer - 11.

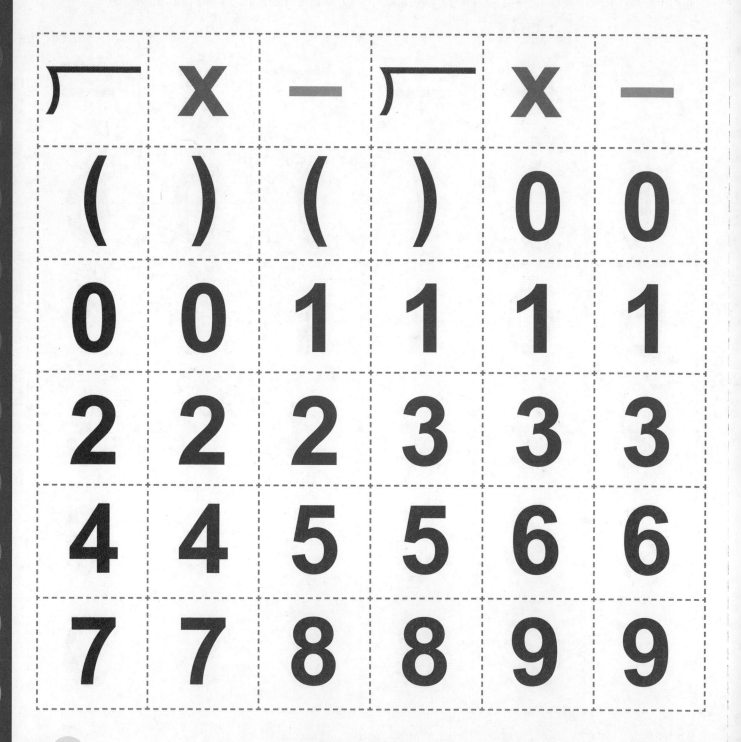

Congratulations!
Great Work!

____

Your Name

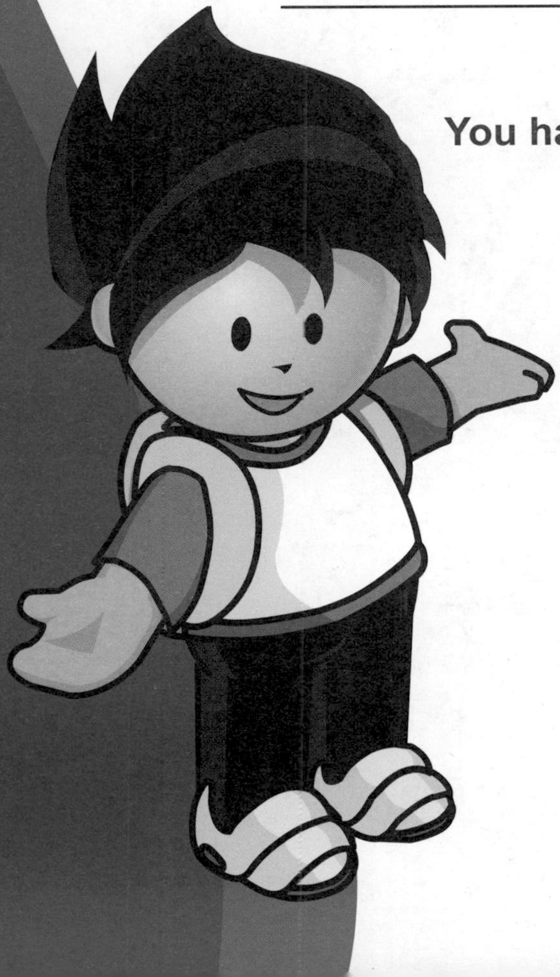

You have successfully completed the requirements for the workbook practice section of:

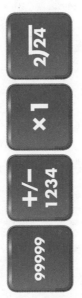

99999 | +/− 1234 | ×1 | 2)24

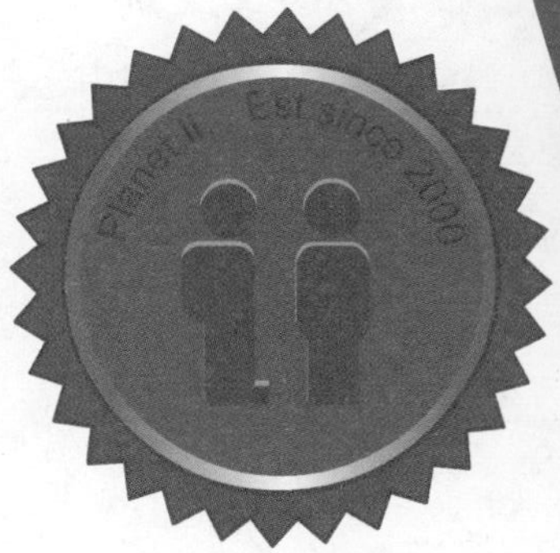

GRADE 3 LEVEL 3
NUMBERS

Professor Mugo

PLANETii Director of Learning

Please enter this code to gain six stars from your SmartMath Practice round. These stars will increase your iiPoints and assist you when you are ready to challenge for this section at

www.britannicasmartmath.com/workbook

3273

login@

www.britannicasmartmath.com/workbook

Measures

This MEASURES section introduces students to both the metric system and US Customary units that can be used to measure length and distance, as well as capacity.

LENGTH AND DISTANCE IV
- Centimeters, Meters, Inches, and Feet
- Learn about and Use Kilometers and Miles
- Measure with Appropriate Units
- Convert Units of Measurement
- Order Units of Measurement
- Measurement Word Problems

CAPACITY
- Introduction to Capacity
- Directly Compare the Capacity of Containers
- Use Improvised Units to Measure the Capacity of Containers
- The Reason for Standard Units
- The Use of Different Measuring Units in Daily Life
- Using Standard Units of Capacity
- Capacity Word Problems

Learn It!

A **millimeter** (**mm**) is a standard metric measuring unit.
Millimeters are used to measure the size of very small objects and very small distances.

The ants are about 30 **mm** apart.

A short way to write **millimeter** is **mm**.

A **millimeter** is smaller than a centimeter.
10 **mm** = 1 cm

A **kilometer** (**km**) is a standard metric measuring unit used to measure very long distances, like the distances between two towns.

Toni's town

1 **km** = 1,000 m

Kira's town

A short way to write **kilometer** is **km**.

A **mile** is a standard customary measuring unit used to measure very long distances.

1 **mile** = 5,280 feet or 1,760 yards

Use It!

Example 1

How many **millimeters** long is the safety pin?
How long is that in centimeters?

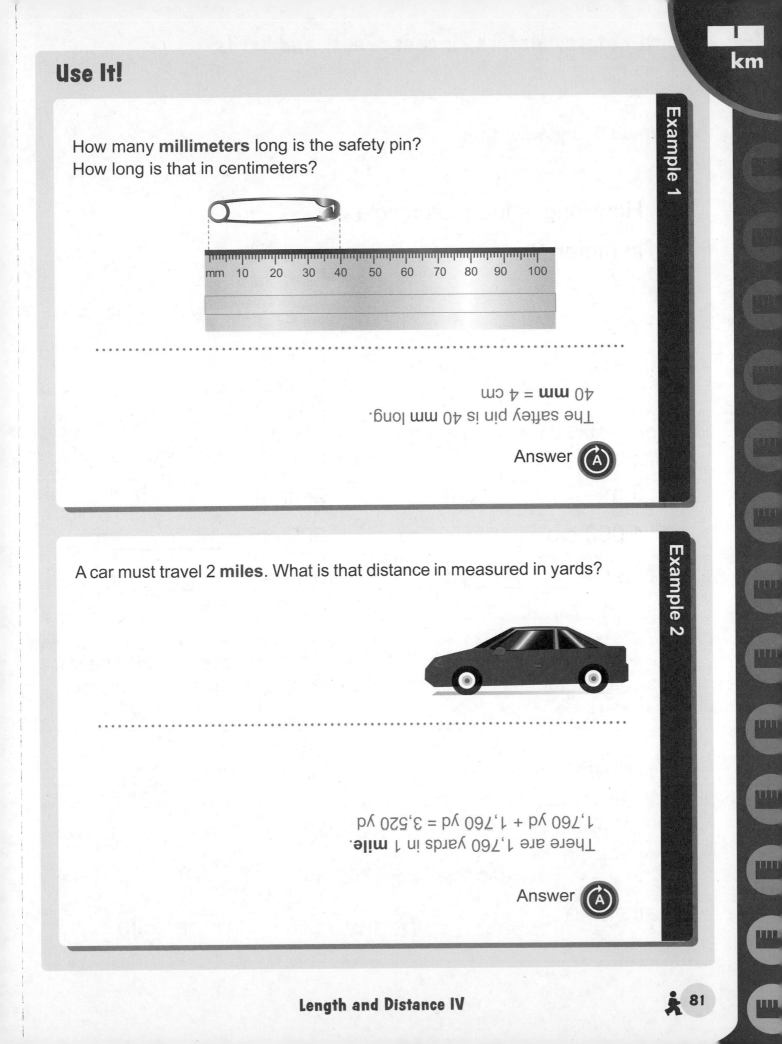

The saffey pin is 40 **mm** long.
40 **mm** = 4 cm

Answer Ⓐ

Example 2

A car must travel 2 **miles**. What is that distance in measured in yards?

There are 1,760 yards in 1 **mile**.
1,760 yd + 1,760 yd = 3,520 yd

Answer Ⓐ

km

Centimeters, Meters, Inches, Feet, and Yards

Write the answer.

How long is the motorcycle in meters?

_____

Convert the units of measurement.

3 m = _____ cm

4,000 cm = _____ m

12 ft = _____ yd

24 in = _____ ft

500 cm = _____ m

5 yd = _____ in

Circle the names of the objects that are best measured in **centimeters**.
Draw a box around the names of the objects that are best measured
in **meters**.

eraser

pen

street

car

boat

horse

bus

airplane

penny

paper clip

Use the map to complete each sentence.

Kilometers are metric units of measurement used to measure long distances, such as the distance between cities.

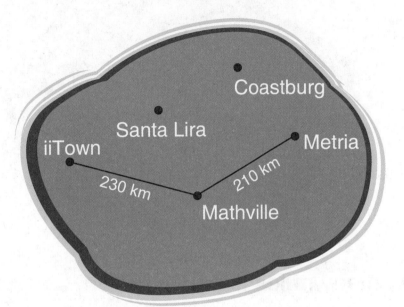

The distance between iiTown and Mathville is _____.

The distance between Mathville and Metria is _____.

The distance from iiTown to Metria, going through Mathville, is _____.

Use the map to answer each question.

Miles are customary units of measurement that are used to measure long distances.

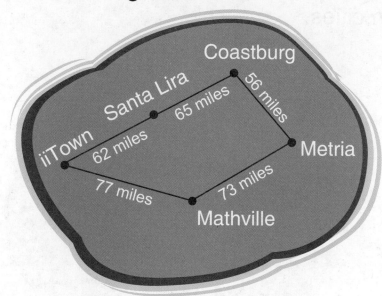

How many **miles** is it from iiTown to Santa Lira? _____

What is the total distance in **miles** from Metria to Coastburg? _____

A delivery truck will travel from iiTown to Santa Lira, and then on to Coastburg.

How many **miles** will it travel in all? _____

Write inches, feet, or **miles** to complete each sentence.

A car is about 12 _____ long.

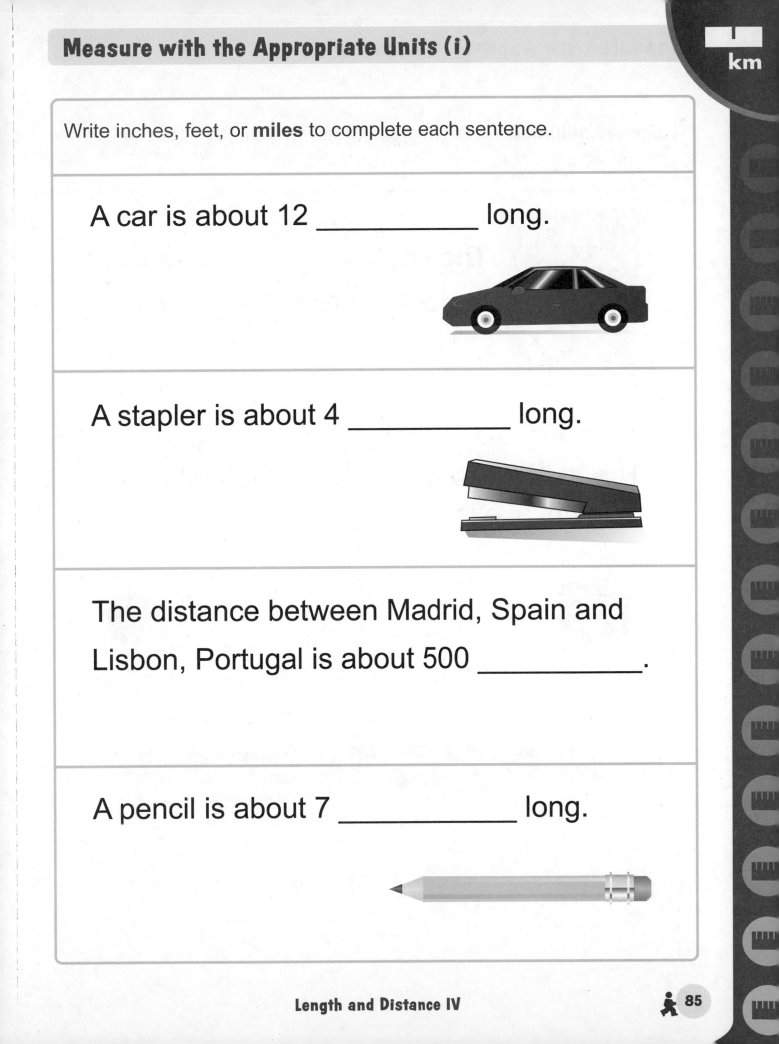

A stapler is about 4 _____ long.

The distance between Madrid, Spain and Lisbon, Portugal is about 500 _____.

A pencil is about 7 _____ long.

Use the **millimeter** ruler on page 105 to answer each question.

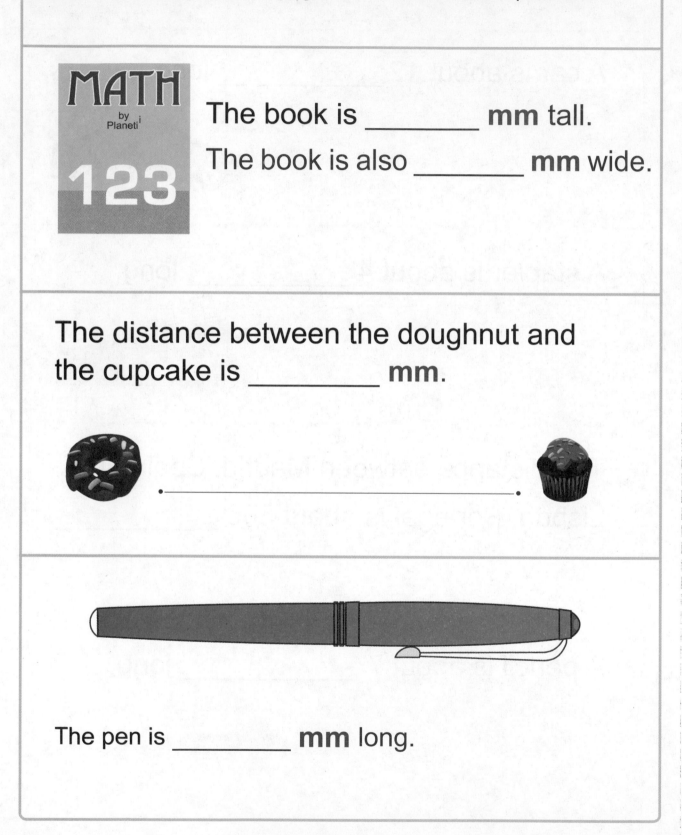

The book is _____ **mm** tall.

The book is also _____ **mm** wide.

The distance between the doughnut and the cupcake is _____ **mm**.

The pen is _____ **mm** long.

Convert Units of Measurement (i)

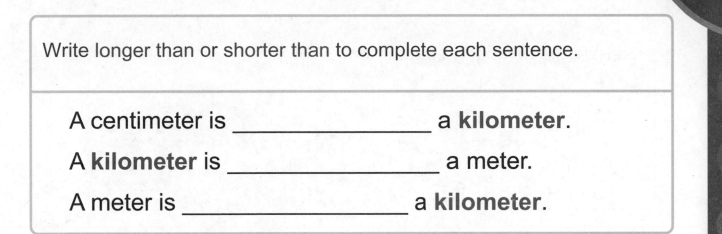

Write longer than or shorter than to complete each sentence.

A centimeter is _____ a **kilometer**.

A **kilometer** is _____ a meter.

A meter is _____ a **kilometer**.

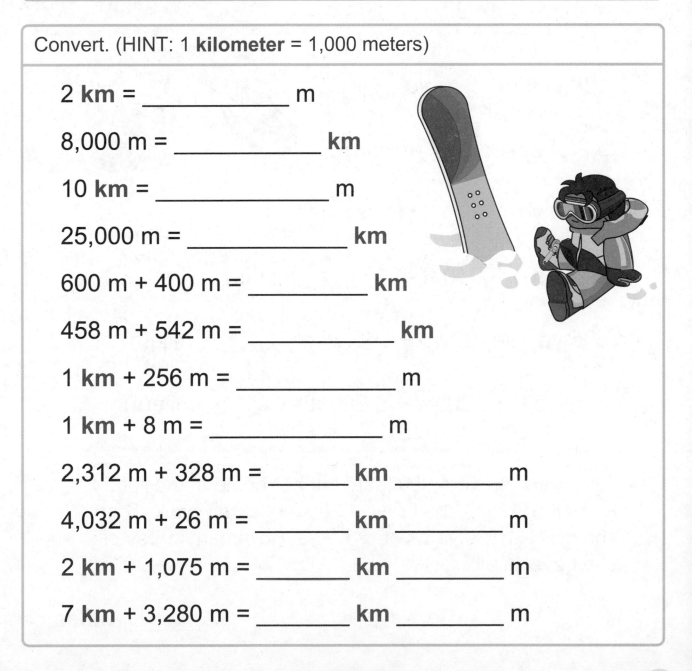

Convert. (HINT: 1 **kilometer** = 1,000 meters)

2 **km** = _____ m

8,000 m = _____ **km**

10 **km** = _____ m

25,000 m = _____ **km**

600 m + 400 m = _____ **km**

458 m + 542 m = _____ **km**

1 **km** + 256 m = _____ m

1 **km** + 8 m = _____ m

2,312 m + 328 m = _____ **km** _____ m

4,032 m + 26 m = _____ **km** _____ m

2 **km** + 1,075 m = _____ **km** _____ m

7 **km** + 3,280 m = _____ **km** _____ m

Convert the units of measurement.

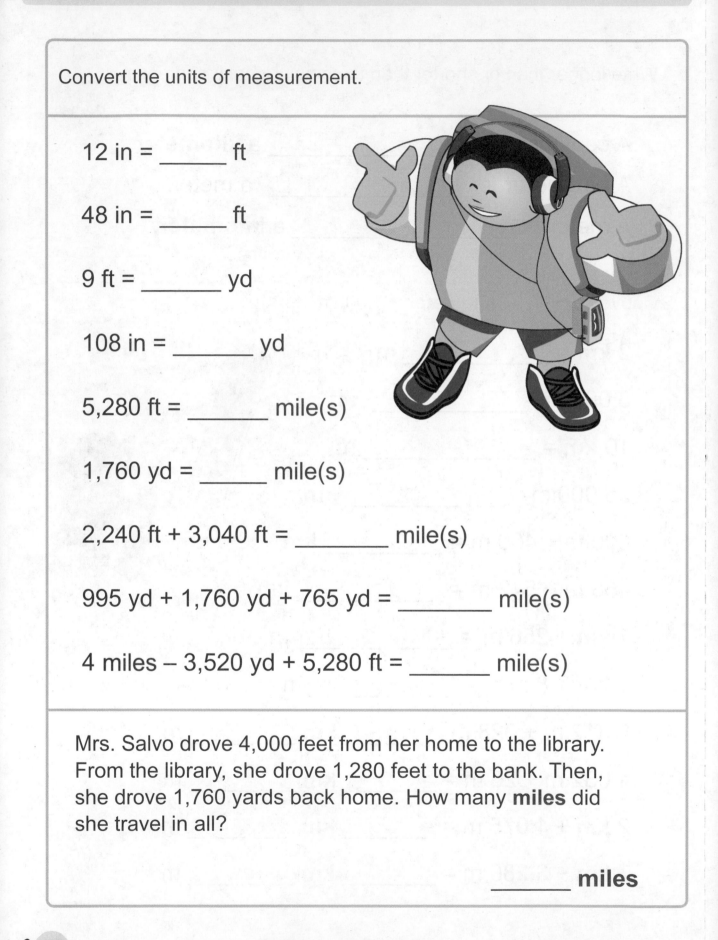

12 in = _____ ft

48 in = _____ ft

9 ft = _____ yd

108 in = _____ yd

5,280 ft = _____ mile(s)

1,760 yd = _____ mile(s)

2,240 ft + 3,040 ft = _____ mile(s)

995 yd + 1,760 yd + 765 yd = _____ mile(s)

4 miles – 3,520 yd + 5,280 ft = _____ mile(s)

Mrs. Salvo drove 4,000 feet from her home to the library. From the library, she drove 1,280 feet to the bank. Then, she drove 1,760 yards back home. How many **miles** did she travel in all?

_____ **miles**

Convert Units of Measurement (iii)

Convert the measurements to solve each problem.

If an envelope is 240 **millimeters** wide, how wide is it in centimeters?

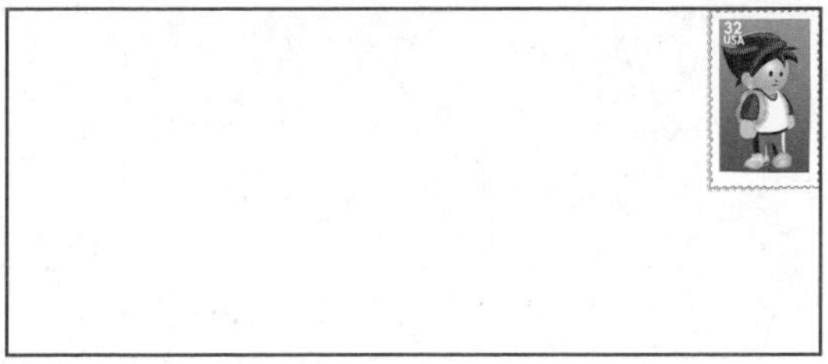

_______ cm

A car will travel 14,000 meters. How far is that in **kilometers**?

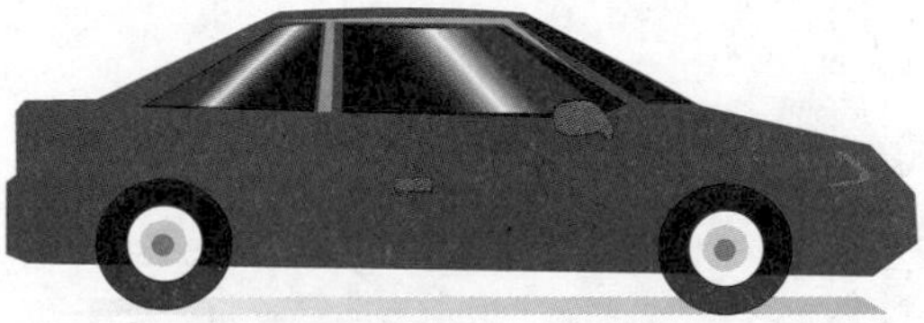

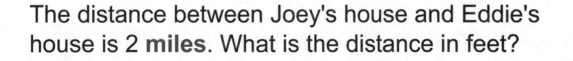

_______ **km**

The distance between Joey's house and Eddie's house is 2 **miles**. What is the distance in feet?

_________ feet

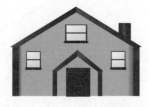

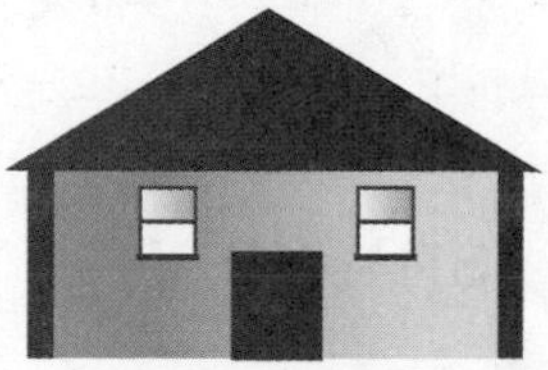

Order Units of Measurement (i)

Write the measurements from **smallest** to **largest**.

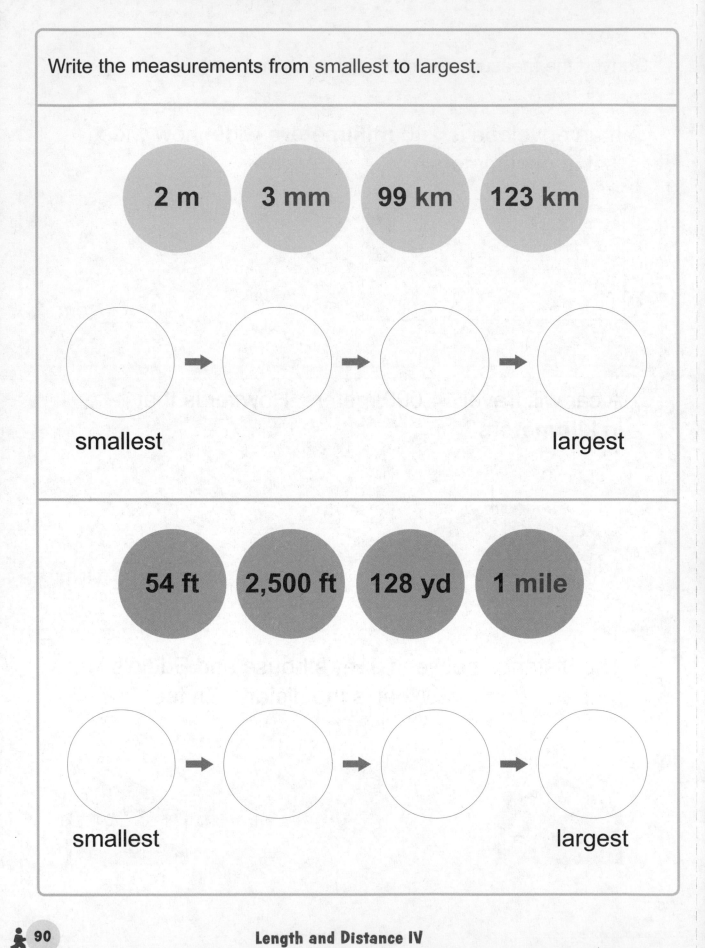

Length and Distance IV

Write the measurements from largest to smallest.

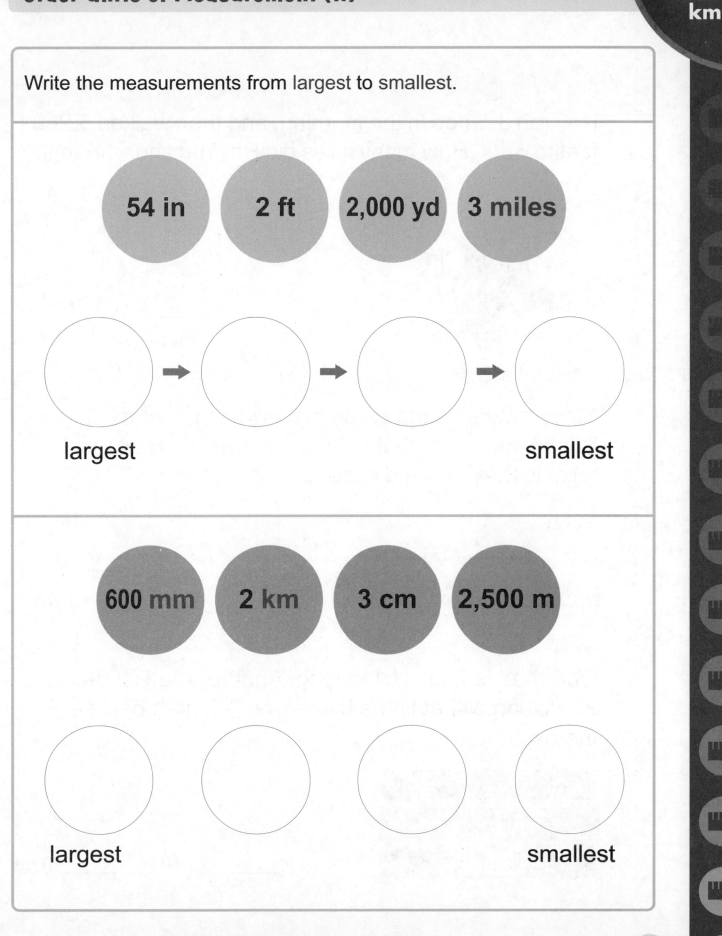

54 in   2 ft   2,000 yd   3 miles

largest → → → smallest

600 mm   2 km   3 cm   2,500 m

largest   smallest

Ray ran 3 **miles** in the morning, and then walked 5,280 feet to work. How many miles did Ray run and walk in all?

_____ miles

Steve made a sand castle that is 42 cm, 7 **mm** tall. Bobby made one that is 35 cm, 9 **mm** tall. How much taller is Steve's sand castle?

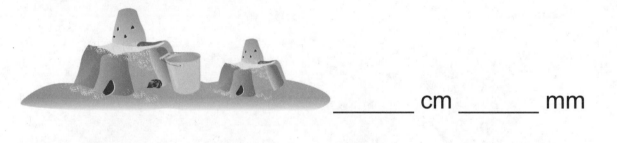

_____ cm _____ mm

One road is 2 **km,** 51 m long. Another road is 1 **km,** 23 m long. What is the difference in length between the two roads?

_____ km _____ m

★ Star Question

Solve.

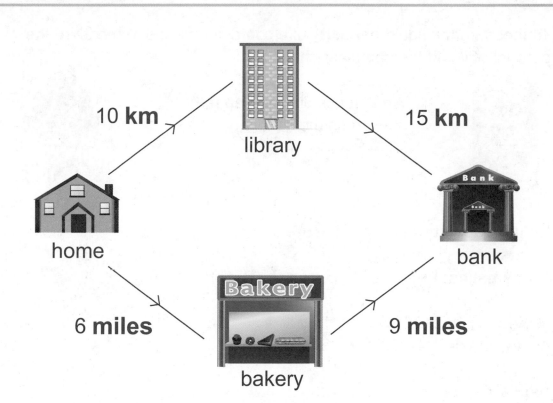

10 **km**

library

15 **km**

home

bank

6 **miles**

Bakery

9 **miles**

bakery

Kelvin wants to drive from his home to the bank.
There are two routes from his home to the bank.

Route 1: Drive from home, past the library, to the bank.
Route 2: Drive from home, past the bakery, to the bank.

If he wants to choose the shortest route, which one
should he choose? (Hint: 5 **miles** equal about 8
kilometers)

Route _____

Learn It!

To measure the liquid **capacity** of a container means to measure the amount of liquid the container can hold.

We can usually find **capacity** labeled on the container.

Liquid **capacity** can be measured in customary units.
The smallest unit is a **fluid ounce** (**fl oz**).

1 measuring **cup** (**c**) = 8 **fl oz**
1 **gallon** (**gal**) = 128 **fl oz** or 16 **c**

Liquid **capacity** can also be measured in metric units.
The smallest unit is a **milliliter** (**mL**).

A drop of water is about 1 **milliliter** (1 **mL**).

There are 1,000 **milliliters** in 1 **liter** (**1 L**).

This soda bottle contains 2 **L**.

Use It!

Example 1

A large glass can hold 2 **cups** of water. How many glasses will it take to fill a 1 **gallon** bucket?

_____

....

It will take 8 glasses to fill the bucket.

$16 \div 2 = 8$

There are 16 **cups** (**c**) in one **gallon** (**gal**).

Answer Ⓐ

Example 2

The metric unit measurement of **capacity** of the can of pear juice

is 330 _____.

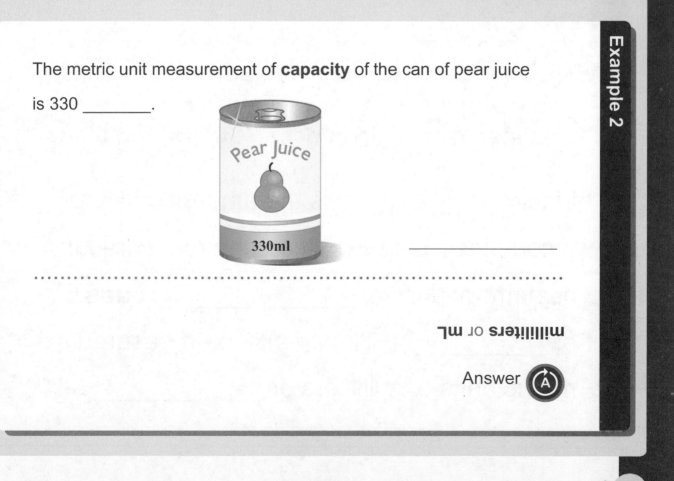

Pear Juice

330ml

_____

....

milliliters or mL

Answer Ⓐ

Write the answer.

David wants to drink milk.
Which container should he
select if he wants to drink a lot of milk?

_____

glass   cup

Write a word from the word bank to complete each sentence.

capacity	fluid ounces	liters	gallons

Liquid _____ is the amount of liquid

a container can hold. It can be measured in

customary units of _____, **cups**,

or _____. It can also be measured in

metric units of milliliters or _____ .

Draw a ✔ in the box below the correct answer to each question.

Which can hold the most liquid?

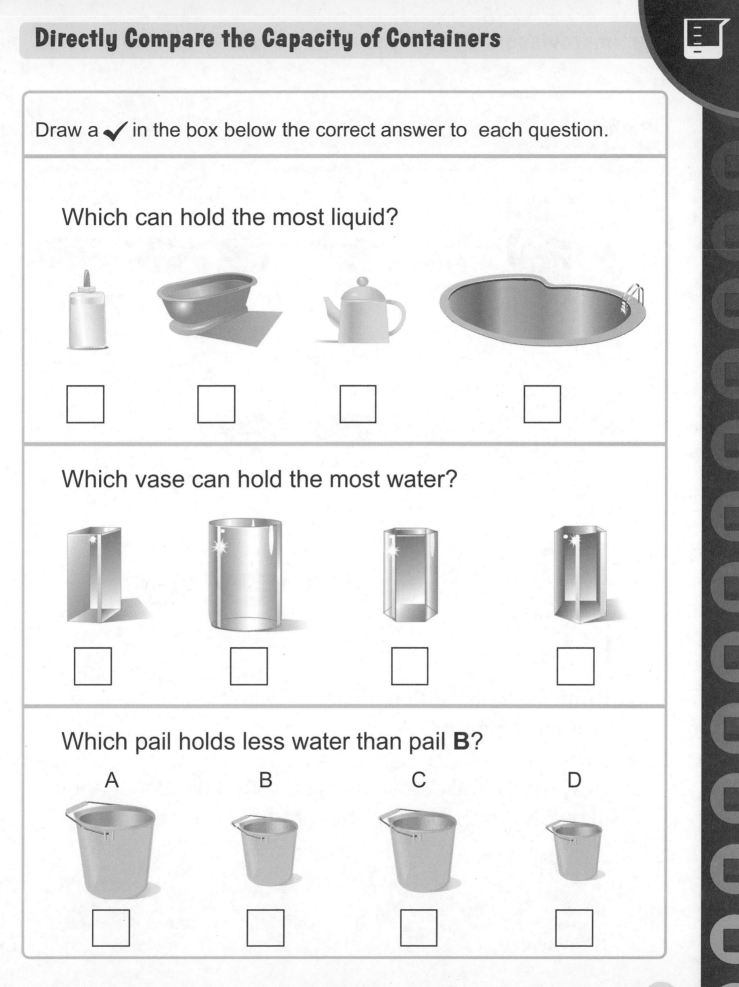

☐   ☐   ☐   ☐

Which vase can hold the most water?

☐   ☐   ☐   ☐

Which pail holds less water than pail **B**?

A   B   C   D

☐   ☐   ☐   ☐

Solve.

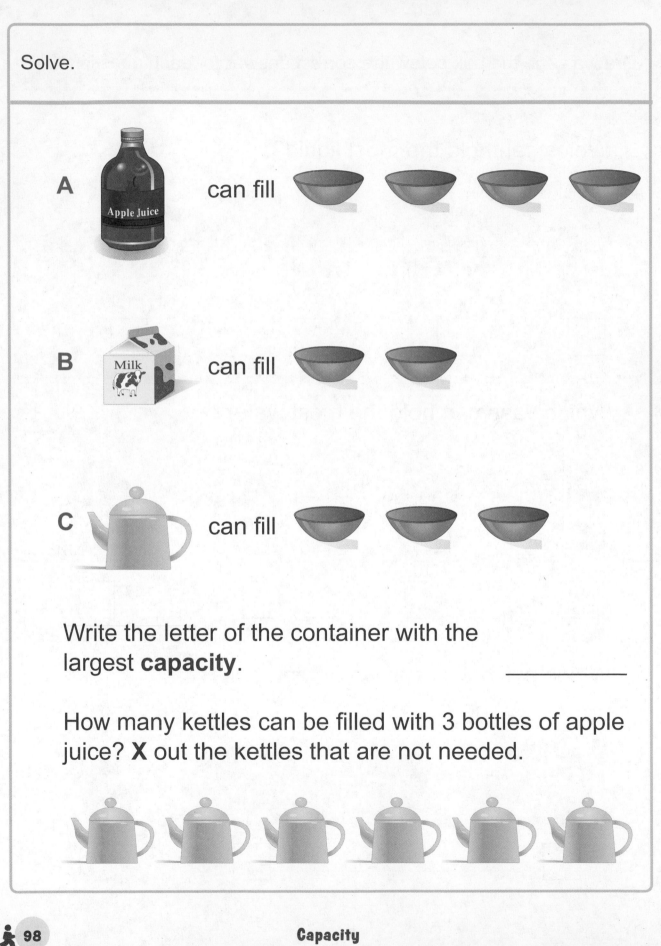

A   can fill

B   can fill

C   can fill

Write the letter of the container with the largest **capacity**.   _____

How many kettles can be filled with 3 bottles of apple juice? **X** out the kettles that are not needed.

Measure, then write the answers.

Measure the **capacity** of your sink with a coffee cup.

_____ coffee cups

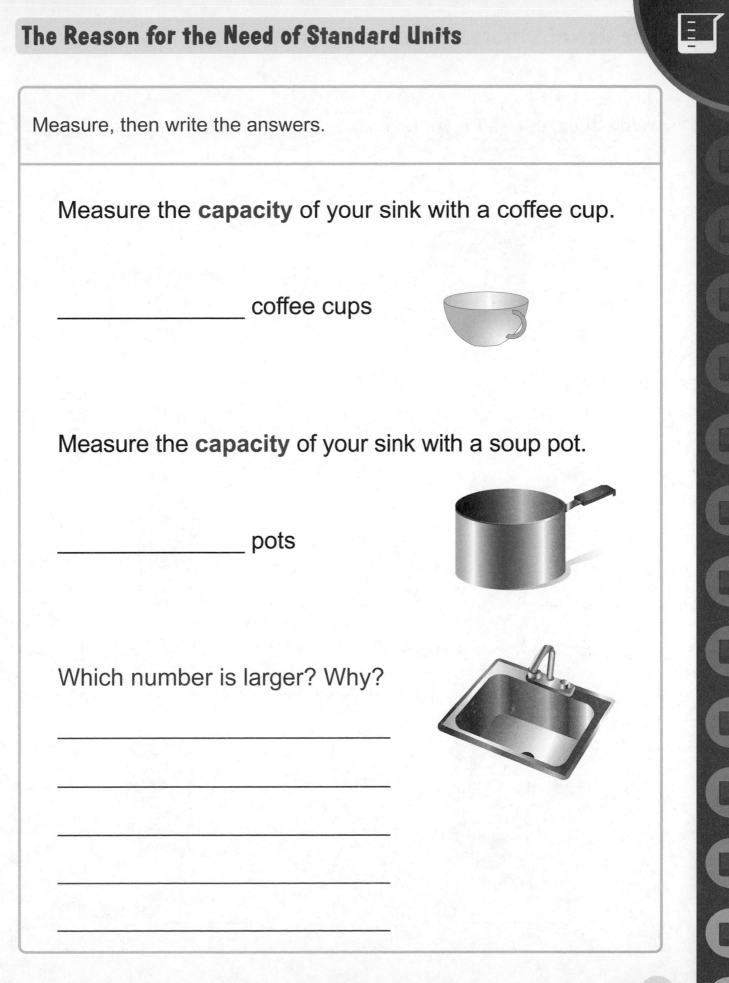

Measure the **capacity** of your sink with a soup pot.

_____ pots

Which number is larger? Why?

_____

_____

_____

_____

The Use of Different Measuring Units in Daily Life

Write **fl oz**, **c**, **gal**, **mL**, or **L** to correctly complete each measurement.

1 _____ of paint

1 _____ of coffee

$\frac{1}{7}$ _____ of water

2 _____ of soda

1 _____ of milk

12 _____ of iced tea

Capacity

Circle the container with the largest **capacity**.

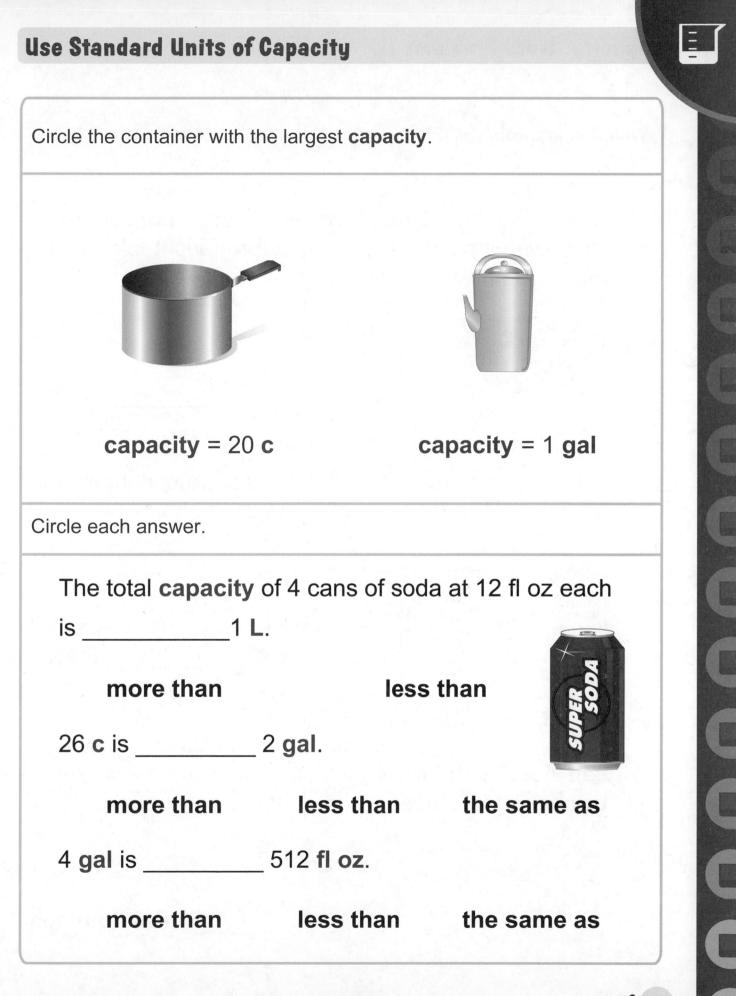

capacity = 20 c   capacity = 1 gal

Circle each answer.

The total **capacity** of 4 cans of soda at 12 fl oz each
is _____ 1 L.

more than   **less than**

26 **c** is _____ 2 **gal**.

more than   **less than**   **the same as**

4 **gal** is _____ 512 **fl oz**.

more than   **less than**   **the same as**

Capacity: Word Problems (i)

Write the answers.

A bowl can hold 2 **cups** of soup. A soup pot can hold 15 bowls of soup. How many **cups** does it take to fill the soup pot?

_____ cups

If 4 identical vases can hold 3 **liters** of water combined, how many **liters** can 12 of these vases hold?

_____ liters

Kevin drinks 4 glasses of milk each day. One glass can hold 10 **fluid ounces** of milk. How many **fluid ounces** of milk does Kevin drink in two weeks?

_____ fluid ounces

Write the answers.

A jug of pear juice has a **capacity** of 5,630 **mL**. A can of pear juice has a **capacity** of 2 **L**. How much more juice can a jug hold than a can?

_____

A glass can hold 22 **fluid ounces** of lemonade. A pitcher can hold 5 **glasses** of lemonade. How many **fluid ounces** does it take to fill up half the pitcher?

_____ **fluid ounces**

A tub can hold 54 **gallons** of water. A pool can hold 4 tubs of water. How many **gallons** of water does it take to fill half the pool?

_____ **gallons**

Star Question

Write **3 gallon** or **5 gallon** to correctly complete the sentences that tell how to measure out 4 **gallons** of water using only a **3 gallon** bucket and a **5 gallon** bucket.

Step 1: Fill the _____ bucket with water.

Step 2: Pour the water into the _____ bucket until it is full.

Step 3: Empty the _____ bucket.

Step 4: Pour the remaining 2 **gallons** of water left in the _____ bucket into the _____ bucket.

Step 5: Fill the _____ bucket with water again.

Step 6: Pour the water into the _____ bucket until it is full.

Now the _____ bucket contains 4 **gallons** of water.

Capacity

Measures Tools Page – Ruler – millimeters

Directions: Cut out the metric rulers pieces along the dashed lines. Tape the pieces together on the blue line. You will notice that the back of the metric ruler includes inch lines, so you can measure in two ways. Use the ruler to measure on page 86. Turn to the back of this page for more ideas on how to use the ruler.

Ideas on how to use the ruler:

1. Find some scrap paper and draw a house that is 200 mm tall from the bottom to the highest roof peak. Draw a door on the house that is 2 in tall by 1 in wide.
   What else can you measure out and draw on the house?
2. Cut out the characters on the page and measure them in mm and inches.

Congratulations!
Great Work!

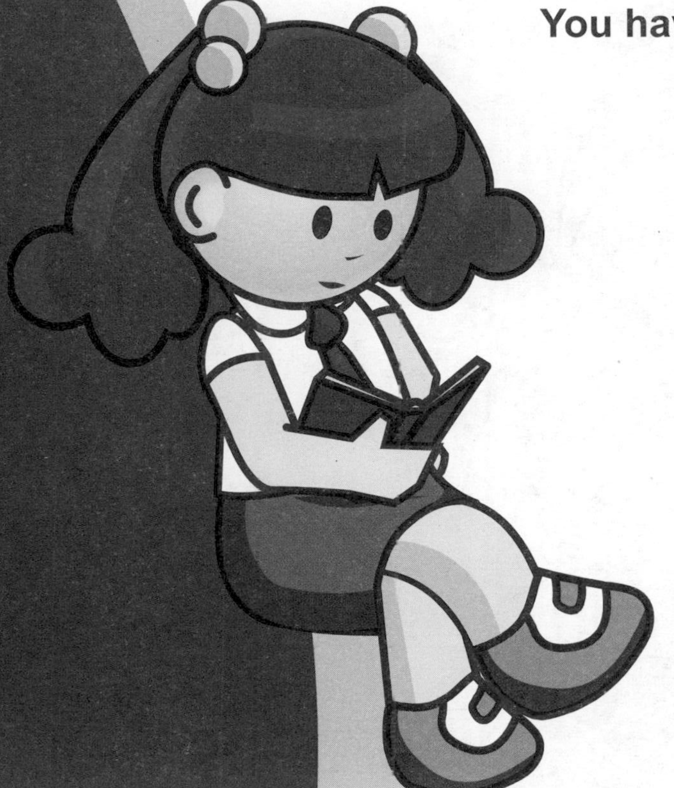

Your Name

You have successfully completed the requirements for the workbook practice section of:

**GRADE 3 LEVEL 3
MEASURES**

Professor Mugo

PLANETii Director of Learning

login @

www.britannicasmartmath.com/workbook

username =

password =

Don't forget to claim your stars and iipoints online.

Shapes and Space

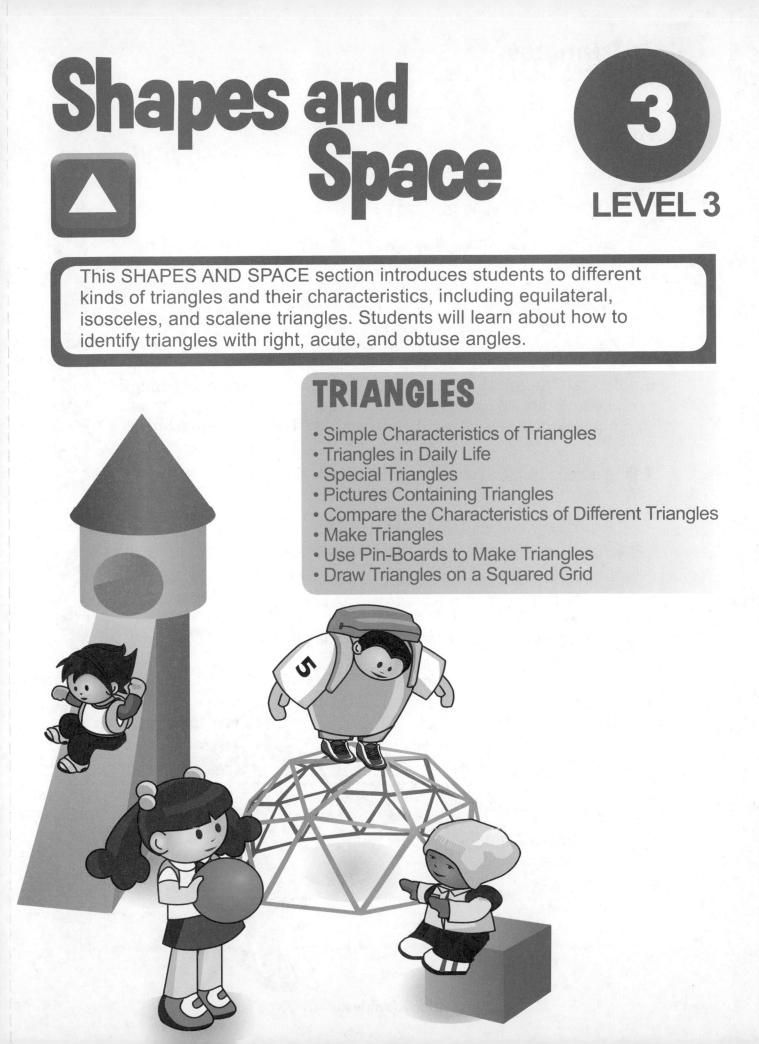

3

LEVEL 3

This SHAPES AND SPACE section introduces students to different kinds of triangles and their characteristics, including equilateral, isosceles, and scalene triangles. Students will learn about how to identify triangles with right, acute, and obtuse angles.

TRIANGLES

- Simple Characteristics of Triangles
- Triangles in Daily Life
- Special Triangles
- Pictures Containing Triangles
- Compare the Characteristics of Different Triangles
- Make Triangles
- Use Pin-Boards to Make Triangles
- Draw Triangles on a Squared Grid

Triangles
LEVEL 3 SHAPES AND SPACE

Learn It!

All triangles have 3 sides and 3 angles.
There are different types of triangles.

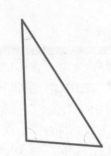

Equilateral Triangle
3 equal sides
3 equal angles

Isosceles Triangle
2 equal sides
2 equal angles

Scalene Triangle
No equal sides
No equal angles

Triangles can also be named according to their angles.

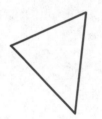

Acute Triangle
3 acute angles

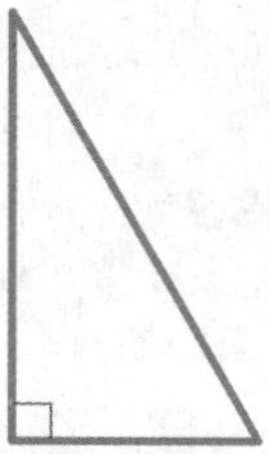

Right-angled Triangle
1 right angle

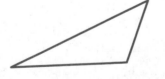

Obtuse Triangle
1 obtuse angle

Use It!

Example 1

Which triangle is an **isosceles right-angled triangle**?

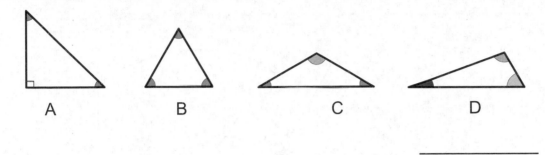

A   B   C   D

_____

···

Figure A is an **isosceles right-angled triangle** because it has two equal sides, two equal angles, and one right angle.

Answer

Example 2

One side of an **equilateral triangle** is 6 cm. What is the total distance around the triangle?

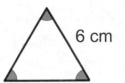
6 cm

_____

···

Since the triangle is an **equilateral triangle**, all 3 sides are equal. Each side is 6 cm. Add. 6 cm + 6 cm + 6 cm = 18 cm. The total distance around the triangle is 18 cm.

Answer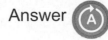

Simple Characteristics of Triangles

Circle the **equilateral triangle**.

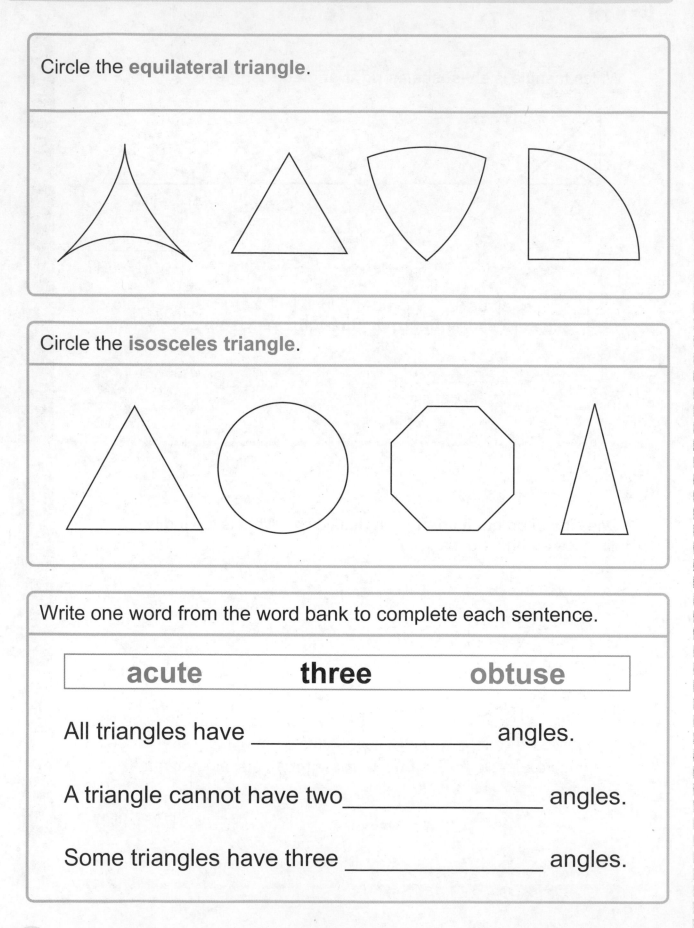

Circle the **isosceles triangle**.

Write one word from the word bank to complete each sentence.

acute	three	obtuse

All triangles have _____ angles.

A triangle cannot have two_____ angles.

Some triangles have three _____ angles.

Triangles in Daily Life

Write the number of triangles found in each 3D shape.

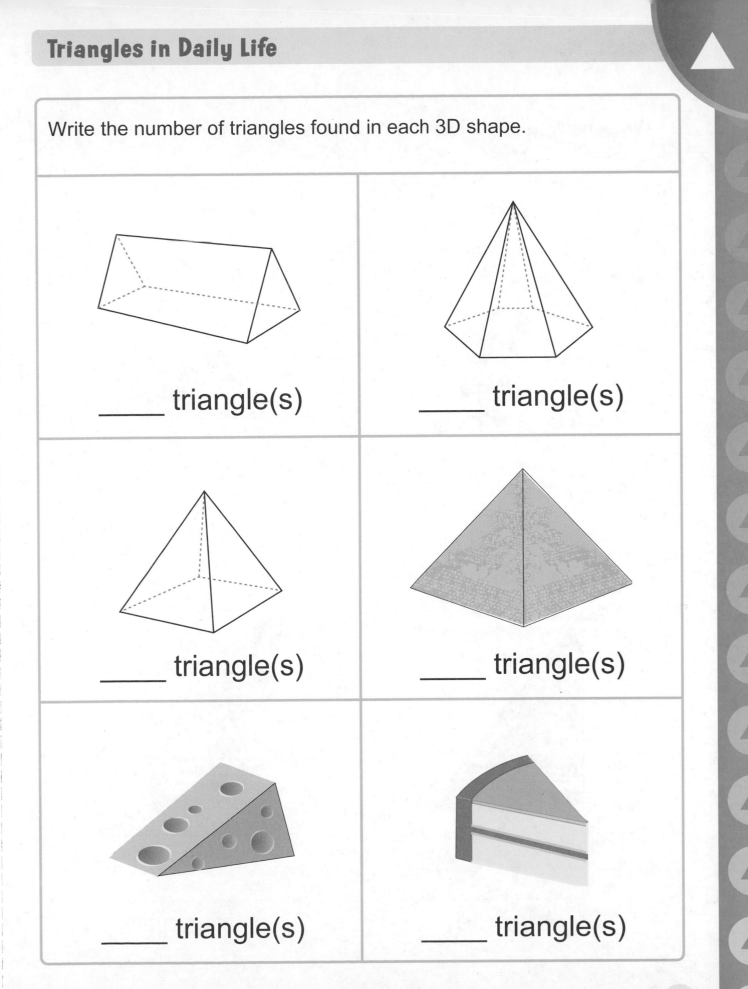

_____ triangle(s)

_____ triangle(s)

_____ triangle(s)

_____ triangle(s)

_____ triangle(s)

_____ triangle(s)

Write the type of triangle each sticker is shaped like.

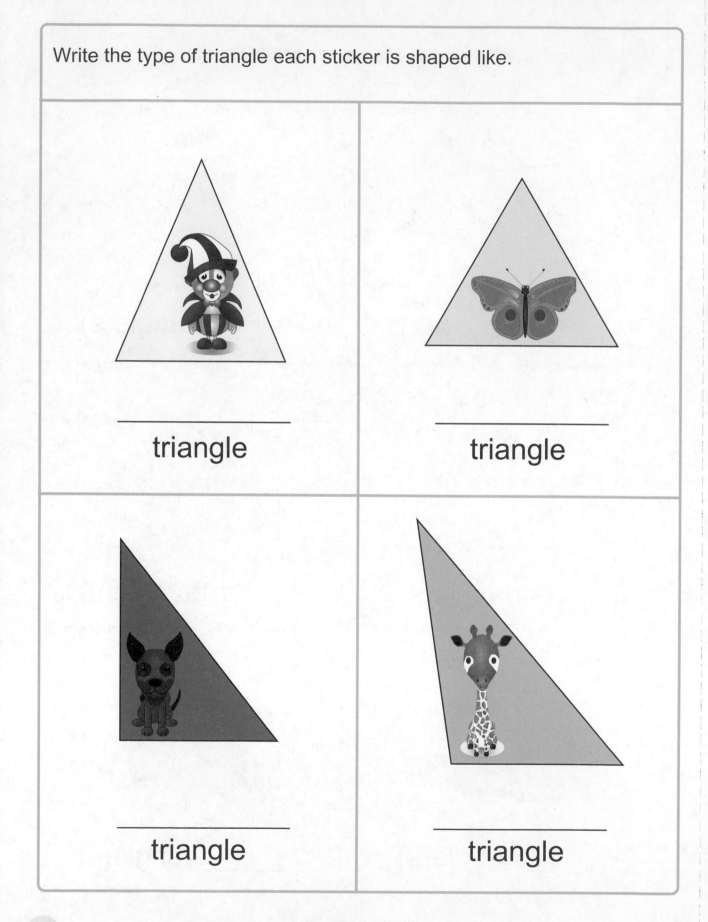

_____
triangle

_____
triangle

_____
triangle

_____
triangle

Count, then write the total number.

How many **right-angled triangles** are there?

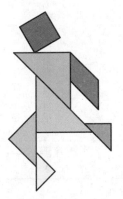

_____

How many **scalene triangles** are there?

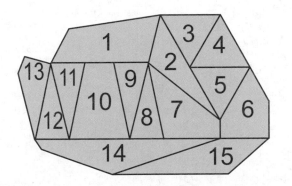

_____

How many **isosceles triangles** are there?

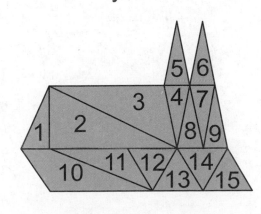

_____

Pictures Containing Triangles (ii)

Color the **right-angled triangles** red. Color the **isosceles triangles** blue. Color the **scalene triangles** purple.

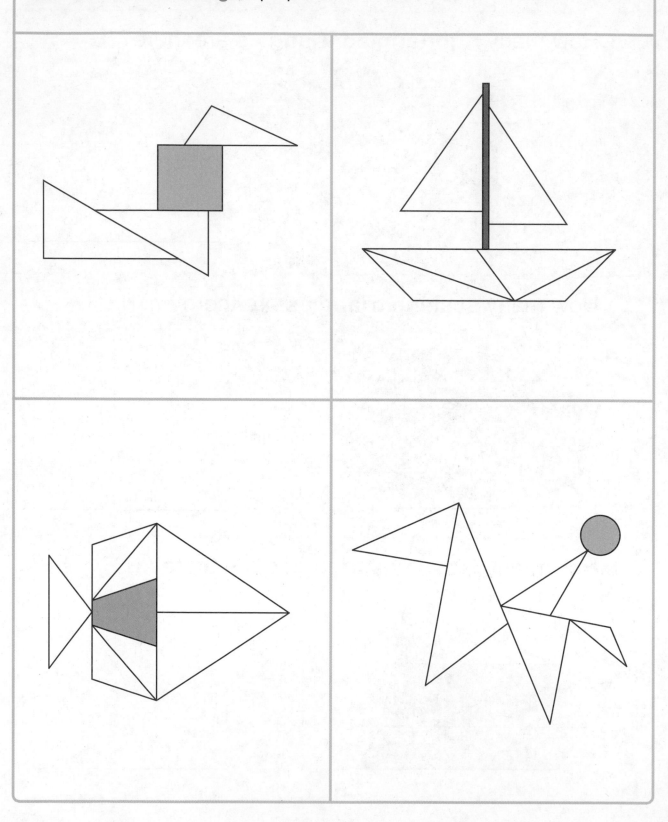

Triangles

Compare the Characteristics of Different Triangles

Draw a ✔ in the box if the triangle always possesses the characteristic.

Characteristic \ Type	Isosceles Triangle	Equilateral Triangle	Right-angled Triangle	Isosceles Right-angled Triangle	Scalene Triangle
3 angles					
3 sides					
no equal sides					
only 2 equal sides					
3 equal sides					
1 right angle					
no right angles					

Triangles

117

Write the number of different triangles formed by connecting the point inside the figure with all the corners of the figure.

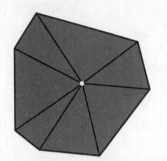

_____

Draw one line from A to D, and one from B to C. Write the number of different types of triangles formed.

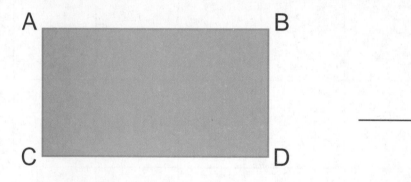

A   B

C   D

_____ different types of triangles

Draw 4 lines on the square to form 8 **isosceles right-angled triangles**.

Draw the named triangle on each pin-board.

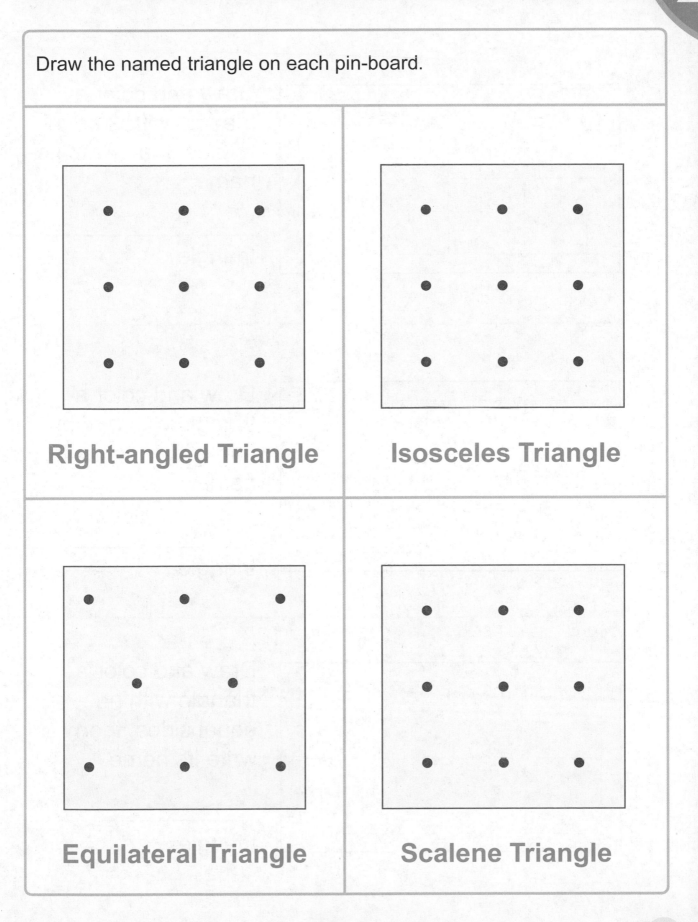

Right-angled Triangle

Isosceles Triangle

Equilateral Triangle

Scalene Triangle

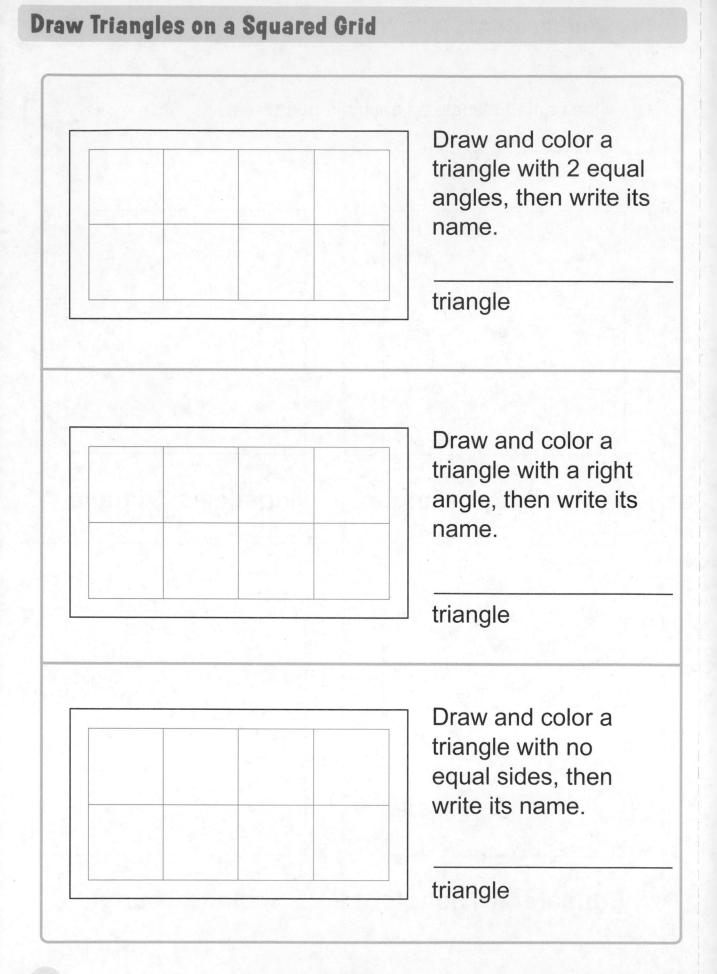

Draw and color a triangle with 2 equal angles, then write its name.

_____

triangle

Draw and color a triangle with a right angle, then write its name.

_____

triangle

Draw and color a triangle with no equal sides, then write its name.

_____

triangle

Star Question

Complete each pattern by drawing and coloring a triangle in the box. Then write its name.

Which triangle comes next in the sequence?

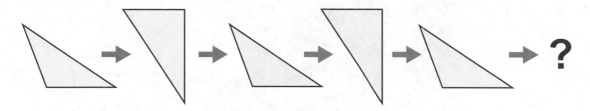

_____ triangle

Which triangle comes next in the sequence?

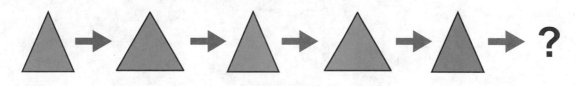

_____ triangle

Shapes and Space Tools

Directions: Cut out the protractor and the triangles along the dashed lines.

How to use the protractor and triangles:
Lay a triangle down on a flat surface. Place the protractor over it so that (1) the inside bottom edge of the protractor lines up exactly with the bottom side of the triangle; and (2) one corner of the triangle lies at the center mark (blue dot) of the protractor. Then, look to see where the side of the triangle within the middle of the protractor lines up against the protractor's curved edge. Is the angle acute, right, or obtuse? Measure all the angles on the triangle. Can you tell what type of triangle it is from measuring its angles?

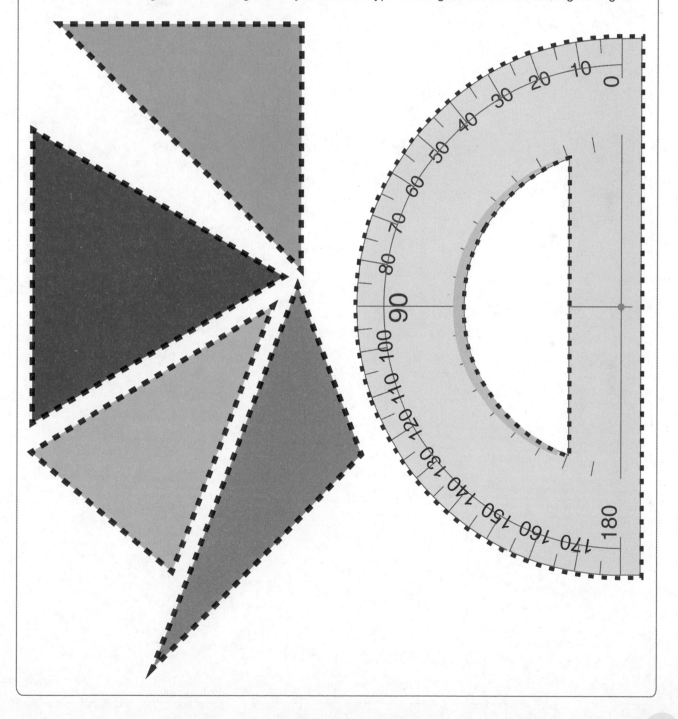

More ideas:

1. Get some scrap paper and draw more triangles. Use the protractor to identify their angles and their types.
2. Bring the triangles with you when you go to the park or a store. How many objects can you see that contain each type of triangle?

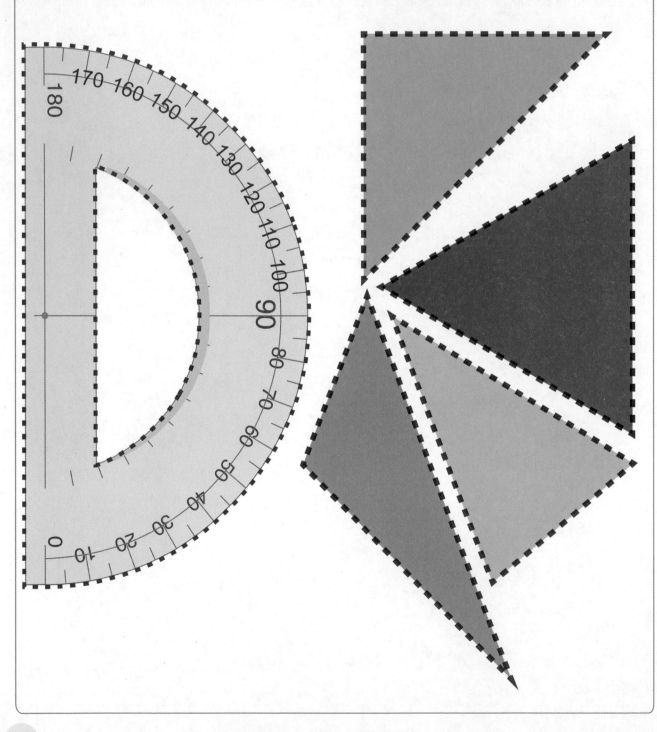

Congratulations!
Great Work!

Your Name

You have successfully completed the requirements
for the workbook practice section of:

GRADE 3 LEVEL 3
SHAPES AND SPACE

Professor Mugo

PLANETii Director of Learning

Est. since 2000

Planetii

login@

www.britannicasmartmath.com/workbook

username =

password =

Don't forget to claim your stars and iipoints online.

Data Handling

This DATA HANDLING section introduces students to advanced block graphs, including how to read and interpret them correctly.

BLOCK GRAPHS

- Interpret Rows and Columns
- Answer Questions about Block Graphs
- Make Block Graphs
- Begin to Estimate Using Block Graphs

Learn It!

Using **block graphs** is a simpler way to represent numbers than using pictograms.

I asked my students: "Which animal do you like the best?"

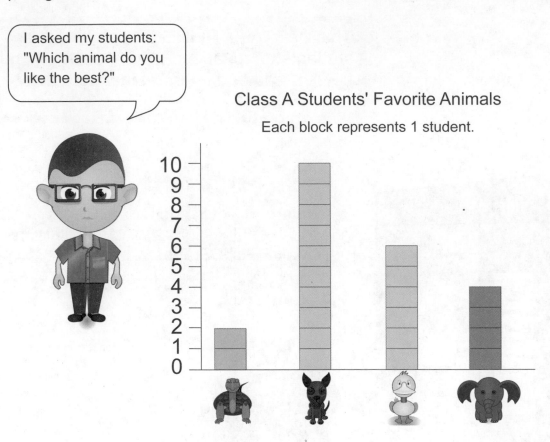

Class A Students' Favorite Animals

Each block represents 1 student.

This **block graph** shows the following information or, **data**:

The most popular animal is the dog.
The least popular animal is the turtle.

There are 2 students who like the turtle.
2 more students like the elephant than the turtle.
There are 22 students in Class A.

Use It!

The following **block graph** records the number of fish caught by each person.

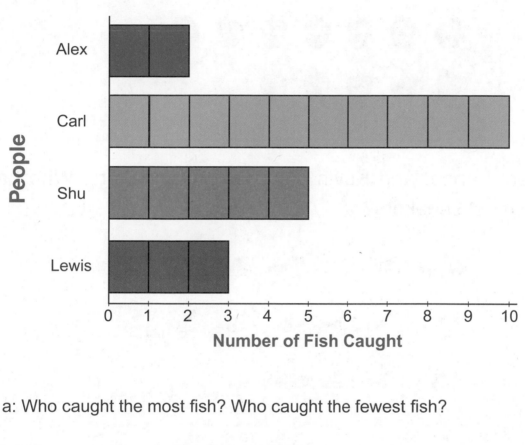

a: Who caught the most fish? Who caught the fewest fish?

b: Who caught 2 more fish than Lewis?

. . . .

a: Carl has the most blocks, so he caught the most fish. Alex has the fewest blocks, so he caught the fewest fish.

b: Lewis caught 3 fish. Shu caught 5 fish. (5 − 3 = 2)
Shu caught 2 more fish than Lewis.

Answer

Interpret Rows and Columns

Write the answers.

Which row of apples is longer?

Row A

Row B

_____

Fred, Lance, and Kevin are counting sneakers. Who has the most sneakers?

Fred

Lance

Kevin

_____

How many trees are there in column 4?

_____

Block Graphs

Use the **block graph** to answer each question.

Joy cleaned out her closet. Here's what she found:

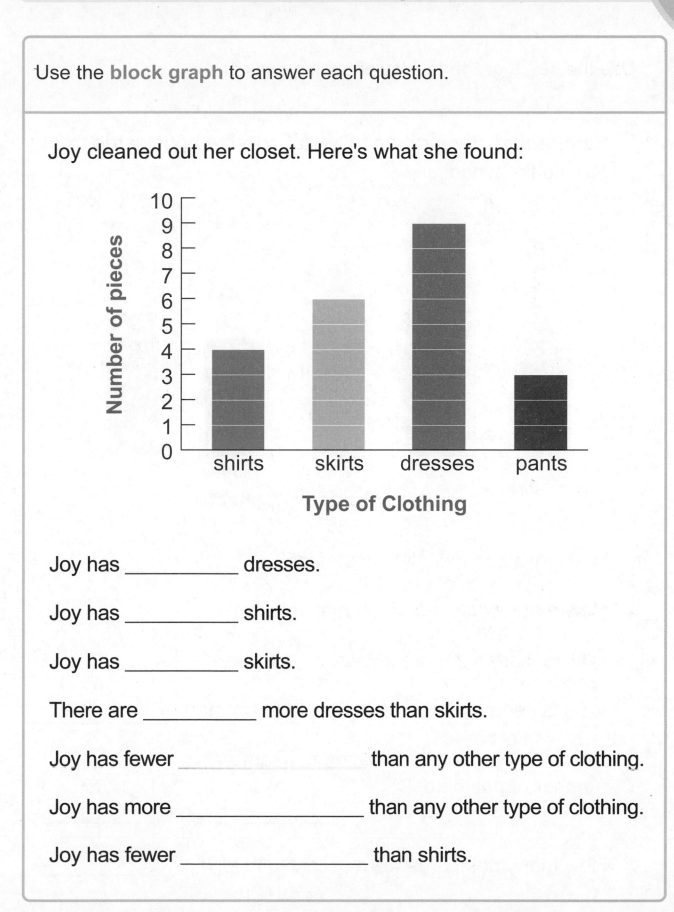

Joy has _____ dresses.

Joy has _____ shirts.

Joy has _____ skirts.

There are _____ more dresses than skirts.

Joy has fewer _____ than any other type of clothing.

Joy has more _____ than any other type of clothing.

Joy has fewer _____ than shirts.

Use the block graph to answer each question.

Sam, Adam, Tamara, and Crystal collected postcards from around the world.

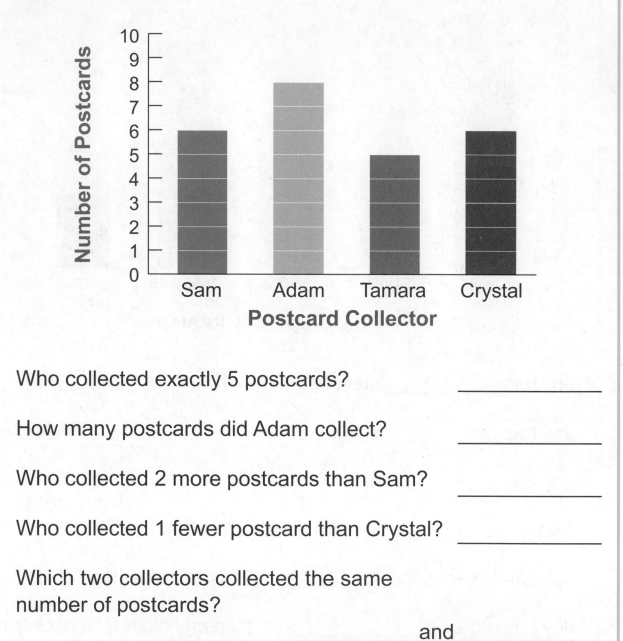

Who collected exactly 5 postcards? _____

How many postcards did Adam collect? _____

Who collected 2 more postcards than Sam? _____

Who collected 1 fewer postcard than Crystal? _____

Which two collectors collected the same number of postcards?

_____ and _____

How many postcards were collected in all? _____

Use the data to complete the block graph.

Four friends went apple picking. Gina picked 5 apples, Lee picked 4 apples, Amy picked 10, and Nia picked 7 apples.

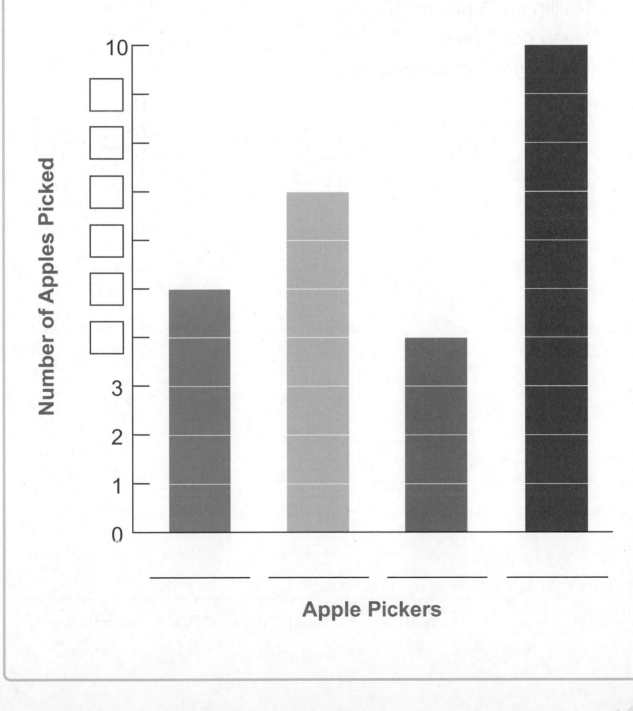

Color the **block graph** according to the **data**.

Ryan, Phillip, Courtney, and Elaine went shopping for candy.

Courtney got 4 pieces of candy.
Phillip got 5 pieces of candy.
Ryan got 7 pieces of candy.
Elaine got 9 pieces of candy.

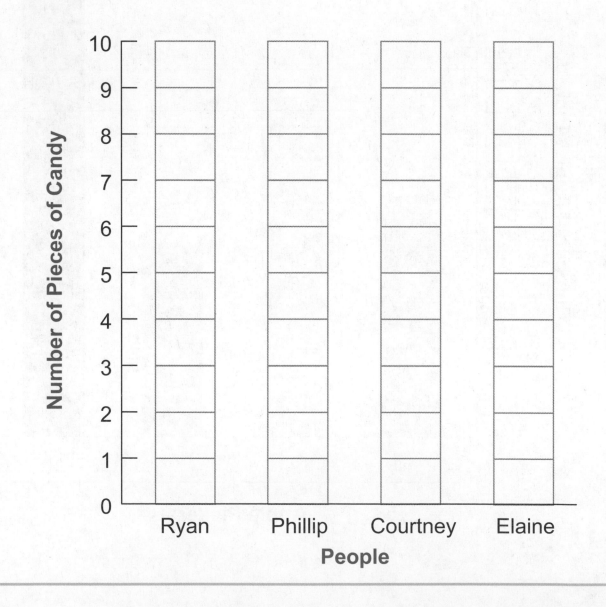

Color to complete the **block graph**, then answer the questions.

Jesse, Mariah, Autumn, and Ethan helped their teacher put away chairs during clean-up time.

Jesse put away 7 chairs.
Mariah put away 8 chairs.
Autumn put away 5 chairs.
Ethan put away 9 chairs.

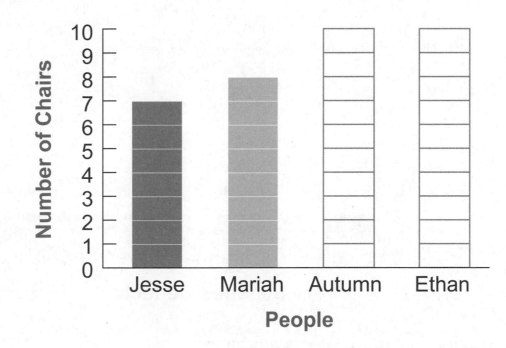

Who put away the most chairs?

Who put away 4 fewer chairs than Ethan?

Which two children put away a combined total of 15 chairs?

_____ and _____

Finish coloring the block graph, then answer the questions.

Freddie, Sarah, Beverly, and Matthew went to the beach to collect seashells.

Freddie collected 6 seashells.
Sarah collected 8 seashells.
Beverly collected 4 seashells.
Matthew collected 7 seashells.

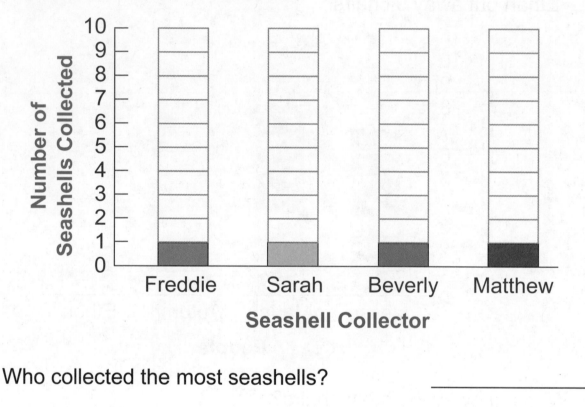

Who collected the most seashells? _____

Who collected the fewest seashells? _____

Who collected 4 more seashells than Beverly? _____

Who collected 2 fewer seashells than Sarah? _____

Read the data, then answer the questions.

The block graph shows the number of times four students each fed the class fish.

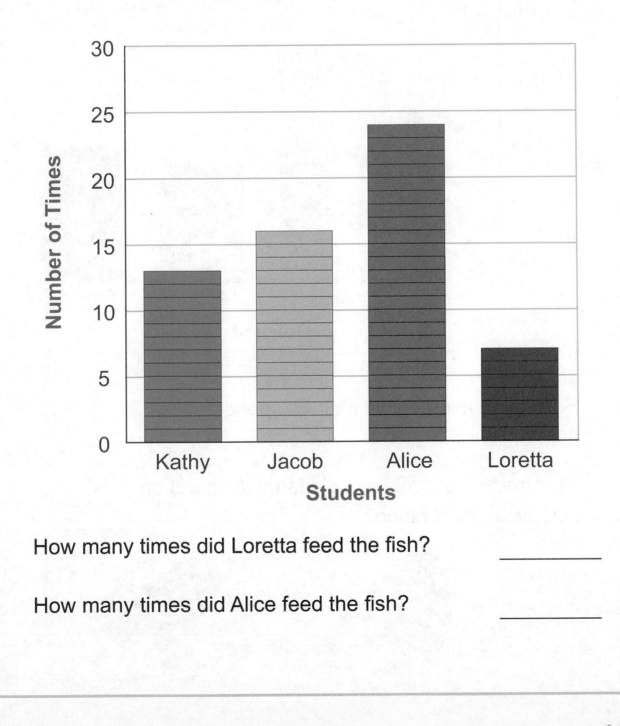

How many times did Loretta feed the fish? _____

How many times did Alice feed the fish? _____

Use the **block graph** to answer each question.

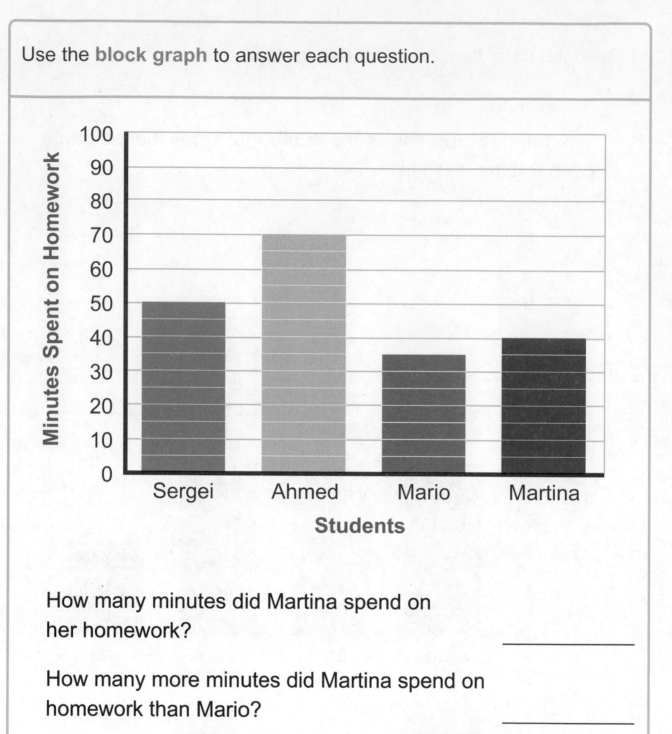

How many minutes did Martina spend on
her homework?

_____

How many more minutes did Martina spend on
homework than Mario?

_____

Block Graphs

Use the **block graph** to answer each question.

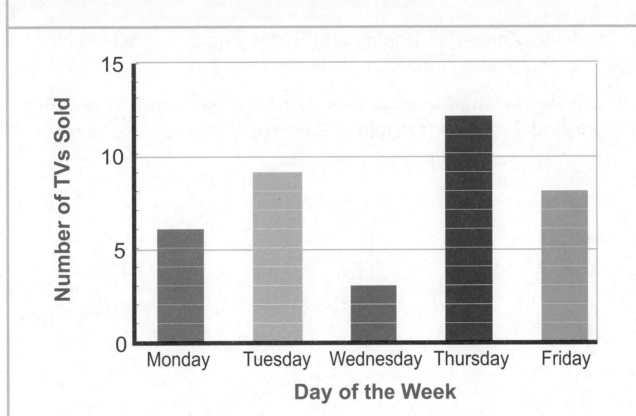

How many TVs were sold
during the week?   _____

How many TVs were sold
on Thursday?   _____

How many TVs were sold
on Tuesday and Wednesday combined?   _____

Were more TVs sold on Monday and Thursday combined or
Tuesday and Wednesday combined?

_____

Star Question

Finsh drawing and coloring the correct number of blocks for each contestant. Then use the **block graph** to answer each question.

Camille, Zachary, Hannah, and Sydney had a contest to see who could finish the most crossword puzzles.

Zachary finished twice as many puzzles as Camille. Hannah finished 4 more puzzles than Zachary, and twice as many as Sydney. Sydney finished 5 puzzles.

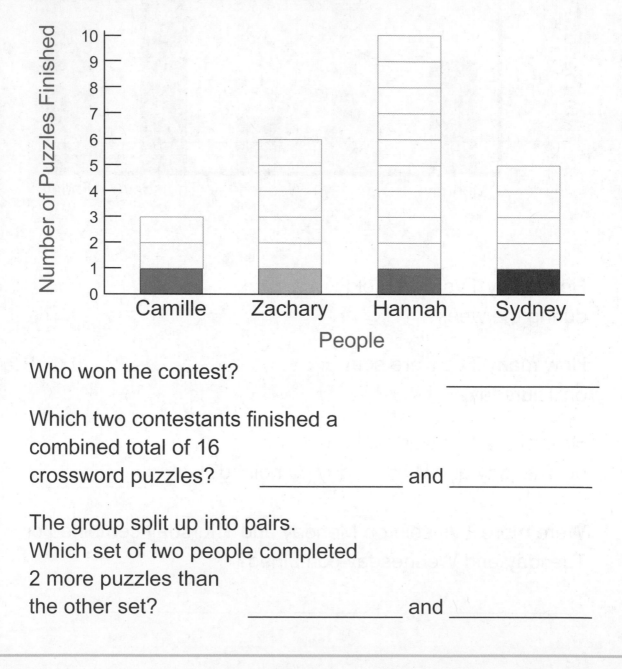

Who won the contest?   _____

Which two contestants finished a
combined total of 16
crossword puzzles?   _____ and _____

The group split up into pairs.
Which set of two people completed
2 more puzzles than
the other set?   _____ and _____

Congratulations!
Great Work!

Est. since 2030

Planet ii

Your Name

You have successfully completed the requirements
for the workbook practice section of:

GRADE 3 LEVEL 3
DATA HANDLING

Professor Muga

PLANETii Director of Learning

Please enter this
code to gain six stars
from your SmartMath Practice
round. These stars will increase
your iiPoints and assist you when
you are ready to challenge for
this section at

www.britannicasmartmath.com/workbook

2512

login @

www.britannicasmartmath.com/workbook

username

password

Don't forget to claim your stars and iipoints online.

4-Digit Numbers

Write each number in number form.

four thousand, seven hundred twenty-three

<u>4,723</u>

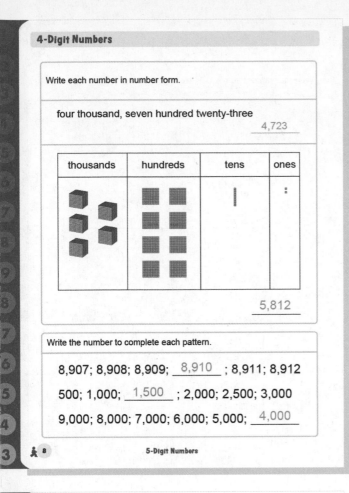

thousands	hundreds	tens	ones

<u>5,812</u>

Write the number to complete each pattern.

8,907; 8,908; 8,909; <u>8,910</u> ; 8,911; 8,912

500; 1,000; <u>1,500</u> ; 2,000; 2,500; 3,000

9,000; 8,000; 7,000; 6,000; 5,000; <u>4,000</u>

8   5-Digit Numbers

Count, Read, and Write 5-Digit Numbers (i)

99999

Write the 5-digit numbers.

10,000	10,000	10,000	10,000
20,000	20,000	20,000	20,000
30,000	30,000	30,000	30,000
40,000	40,000	40,000	40,000
50,000	50,000	50,000	50,000
60,000	60,000	60,000	60,000
70,000	70,000	70,000	70,000
80,000	80,000	80,000	80,000
90,000	90,000	90,000	90,000

5-Digit Numbers   9

Count, Read, and Write 5-Digit Numbers (ii)

Match each number with its word form.

10,000 •   • seventy thousand

20,000 •   • ten thousand

30,000 •   • eighty thousand

40,000 •   • fifty thousand

50,000 •   • thirty thousand

60,000 •   • twenty thousand

70,000 •   • ninety thousand

80,000 •   • forty thousand

90,000 •   • sixty thousand

10   5-Digit Numbers

Count, Read, and Write 5-Digit Numbers (iii)

99999

Write each number in word form.

67,982

<u>Sixty-seven thousand, nine hundred eighty-two</u>

45,203

<u>Forty-five thousand, two hundred three</u>

79,115

<u>Seventy-nine thousand, one hundred fifteen</u>

34,822

<u>Thirty-four thousand, eight hundred twenty-two</u>

19,676

<u>Nineteen thousand, six hundred seventy-six</u>

5-Digit Numbers   11

Answer Key

143

Count, Read, and Write 5-Digit Numbers (iv)

Write each number in number form.

forty-five thousand, six hundred six	45,606
seventy-two thousand, nine hundred twenty-three	72,923
thirteen thousand, eight hundred forty-one	13,841
sixty thousand, five hundred thirty-two	60,532
ninety-nine thousand, four hundred fifty-three	99,453

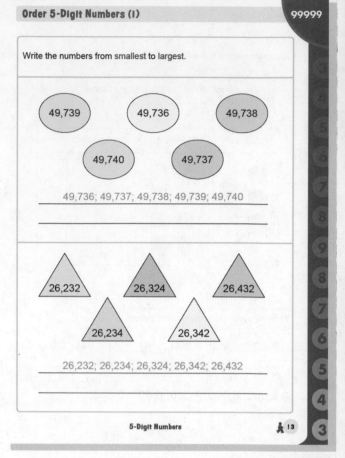

Order 5-Digit Numbers (i)

Write the numbers from smallest to largest.

49,739   49,736   49,738   49,740   49,737

49,736; 49,737; 49,738; 49,739; 49,740

26,232   26,324   26,432   26,234   26,342

26,232; 26,234; 26,324; 26,342; 26,432

Order 5-Digit Numbers (ii)

Write the numbers from largest to smallest.

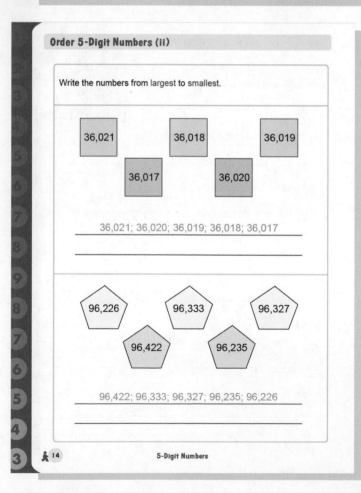

36,021   36,018   36,019   36,017   36,020

36,021; 36,020; 36,019; 36,018; 36,017

96,226   96,333   96,327   96,422   96,235

96,422; 96,333; 96,327; 96,235; 96,226

5-Digit Place Values (i)

Write the digit in the ten thousands place.

45,920	4	29,189	2
67,547	6	89,316	8
98,346	9	59,010	5

Write the place value of the underlined digit.

64,000	hundreds	place
59,738	thousands	place
32,798	ten thousands	place
14,921	tens	place
27,349	ten thousands	place
78,466	thousands	place
93,584	ten thousands	place
63,919	ones	place

Answer Key

5-Digit Place Values (ii)

Complete each number sentence.

86,344 = __80,000__ + 6,000 + __300__ + 40 + __4__

__42,056__ = 40,000 + 2,000 + 50 + 6

27,981 = 20,000 + __7,000__ + 900 + __80__ + 1

54,073 = __50,000__ + 4,000 + __70__ + 3

Write what must be done to change each number on the left to the number at its right.

13,456 ➡ 18,456	Add __5__ to the __thousands__ place.
12,756 ➡ 32,756	Add __2__ to the __ten thousands__ place.
57,053 ➡ 57,853	Add __8__ to the __hundreds__ place.

16   5-Digit Numbers

5-Digit Place Values (iii)

99999

Write the numbers.

A number with a 3 in the ones place, a 7 in the tens place, a 0 in the hundreds place, a 9 in the thousands place, and a 1 in the ten thousands place.

__19,073__

A number with a 2 in the ten thousands place, a 4 in the ones place, a 3 in the hundreds place, a 8 in the tens place. and a 6 in the thousands place.

__26,384__

A number with a 4 in the hundreds place, a 2 in the tens place, a 7 in the ten thousands place, a 5 in the ones place, and a 9 in the thousands place.

__79,425__

A number with a 5 in the tens place, a 4 in the hundreds place, an 8 in the ones place, a 3 in the ten thousands place, and a 1 in the thousands place.

__31,458__

A number with a 0 in the thousands place, a 5 in the tens place, a 4 in the ten thousands place, a 1 in the ones place, and a 2 in the hundreds place.

__40,251__

5-Digit Numbers   17

5-Digit Numbers: Word Problems (i)

Mindy has $35,682 in her bank account. She wants to buy a car that costs $36,682. How much more money does Mindy need to buy the car?

```
  36682
− 35682
  1,000
```
$1,000

Jesse collects puzzle pieces. He has a total of 23,500 pieces. How many more puzzle pieces does he need to reach 25,500 puzzle pieces?

```
  25500
− 23500
  2,000
```
__2,000__ pieces

Felicia and Robin are playing a video game. Felicia has 15,000 points and Robin has 20,000 points. If they combine their points, how many total points will they have?

```
  20000
+ 15000
  35,000
```
__35,000__ points

18   5-Digit Numbers

5-Digit Numbers: Word Problems (ii)

99999

Justin and Jim have been collecting baseball cards for eleven years. Justin has a total of 12,000 baseball cards and Jim has a total of 16,000 baseball cards. How many baseball cards do they have in all?

```
  12000
+ 16000
  28,000
```
__28,000__ cards

Susie's parents bought a new boat. The boat cost $19,500. Susie knows that their old boat cost $14,500. How much more does the new boat cost than the old boat cost?

```
  19500
− 14500
  5,000
```
$5,000 more

Each shipment of toys to Tina's Toy Store contains 10,000 boxes. How many boxes do 3 shipments contain?

```
  10000
  10000
+ 10000
  30,000
```
__30,000__ boxes

5-Digit Numbers   19

Answer Key

145

Use the numbers in the bubble to solve the problem.

6 5 8 4 2

I am a **5-digit number** made up of 4 even-numbered digits and 1 odd-numbered digit.

The number in my **ten thousands** place is the largest digit, and my thousands place has the smallest digit.

My tens digit is 2 more than my thousands digit and 2 less than my ones digit.

My hundreds digit is the sum of the other 4 digits divided by 4.

What number am I? __82,546__

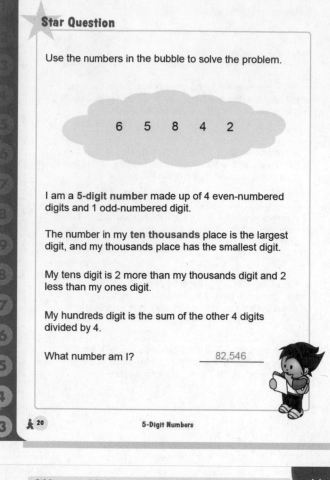

Learn It!

Here is how to add 4-digit numbers with regrouping.

Step 1: Add the ones.
Regroup if needed, carrying 10 ones to the tens place.

Step 2: Add the tens.
Regroup if needed, carrying 10 tens to the hundreds place.

Step 3: Add the hundreds.
Regroup if needed, carrying 10 hundreds to the thousands place.

Step 4: Add the thousands.

Example:

3277 + 1536 = ?

		1	1	
Th	H	T	O	
3,	2	7	7	
+ 1,	5	3	6	
4,	8	1	3	

Step 1: Ones place: 7 + 6 = 13.
Keep the 3 and carry the 10.

Step 2: Tens place: 10 + 70 + 30 = 110.
Keep the 10 and carry the 100.

Step 3: Hundreds place: 100 + 200 + 500 = 800

Step 4: Thousands place: 3,000 + 1,000 = 4,000

Commutative Property of Addition: Numbers can be added in any order.
3000 + 1000 = 1000 + 3000

Associative Property of Addition: Numbers that are added can be grouped in any order.
(100 + 200) + 500 = 100 + (200 + 500)

Answer: 4,000 + 800 + 10 + 3 = 4,813

Addition with 4-Digit Numbers

Solve.

```
  2 5 0       4 5 3       2 4 8
+   1 7     + 4 5 6     + 3 1 7
  2 6 7       9 0 9       5 6 5

  4 7 9       5 9 4       6 0 6
- 3 5 6     -   3 8     - 2 4 1
  1 2 3       5 5 6       3 6 5
```

Jerry's pet store has 401 goldfish. Charlie's pet store has 263 more goldfish than Jerry's. Adrian's pet store has 318 fewer goldfish than Charlie's. How many goldfish does Adrian's pet store have?

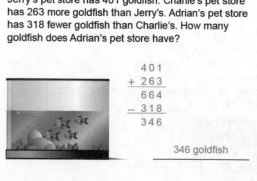

```
    4 0 1
  + 2 6 3
    6 6 4
  - 3 1 8
    3 4 6
```

__346 goldfish__

Addition within Four Places

Add.

```
  3 2 5 0       2 6 3 1       3 0 4 7
+   3 4 6     + 5 3 5 2     + 5 8 1 1
  3, 5 9 6      7, 9 8 3      8, 8 5 8

      1             1             1
  5 1 8 2       7 0 3 9       1 5 6 6
+ 3 6 7 5     + 1 9 2 3     + 4 6 2 3
  8, 8 5 7      8, 9 6 2      6, 1 8 9

      1           1   1         1 1
  3 5 1 0       4 9 5 3       2 3 5 1
+   1 9 9     + 1 4 2 7     + 6 6 5 2
  3, 7 0 9      6, 3 8 0      9, 0 0 3

  1 1 1         1 1 1         1 1 1
  3 6 8 9       1 6 8 5       3 9 6 4
+   9 1 1     + 6 6 7 9     + 1 0 9 8
  4, 6 0 0      8, 3 6 4      5, 0 6 2
```

Answer Key

Subtraction within Four Places

+/−
1234

Subtract.

```
  3260          9152          4856
−  230        − 2041        − 2314
  3,030         7,111         2,542

  1627          7787          3516
−  903        − 3729        − 2054
   724          4,058         1,462

  1460          3798          5138
− 1172        − 1809        − 3247
   288          1,989         1,891

  2000          4860          2673
−  747        − 2895        − 1986
  1,253         1,965          687
```

Addition and Subtraction IV   27

Adding Three Numbers within Four Places

Add.

```
  1324          3425          1034
   302          1403          4223
+  211        + 2160        + 1312
  1,837         6,988         6,569

     1             1           1  1
  1283          2630          4851
  3024          3412          1505
+ 1462        + 2535        + 2628
  5,769         8,577         8,984

   1 1          1 1 2         1 1 1
  2615          1546          2630
  1065          2638          3564
+ 1179        + 4059        + 1346
  4,859         8,243         7,540
```

28   Addition and Subtraction IV

Mixed Operations: Addition and Subtraction

+/−
1234

Solve from left to right.

1397 + 2401 − 3294 = __504__

5835 − 1729 + 2743 = __6,849__

2517 + 1945 − 3051 = __1,411__

2642 + 3695 − 4870 = __1,467__

4286 − 2977 + 1708 = __3,017__

5000 − 2306 + 4123 = __6,817__

3658 + 4796 − 2999 = __5,455__

1692 + 3368 − 5060 = __0__

1926 − 1347 + 3175 = __3,754__

Addition and Subtraction IV   29

Commutative and Associative Properties of Addition (I)

Write the number to complete each equation. Then, write A for Associative or C for Commutative in the box to name the property shown in each equation.

692 + (258 + 951) = (692 + __258__) + 951   [A]

(198 + 501) + 538 = 198 + (501 + __538__)   [A]

3089 + 2641 = 2641 + __3089__   [C]

3725 + 2864 = __2864__ + 3725   [C]

Compare the two statements. If they are equal, write =. If they are not equal, write ≠.

742 − (315 + 139) __=__ 742 − (139 + 315)

228 + (231 + 108) __≠__ 228 + (231   108)

187 + 264 + 315 __=__ 264 + 187 + 315

(428 − 196) + 119 __=__ 119 + (428 − 196)

127 + 352 + 648 + 258 __=__ 127 + (352 + 648) + 258

30   Addition and Subtraction IV

Answer Key

147

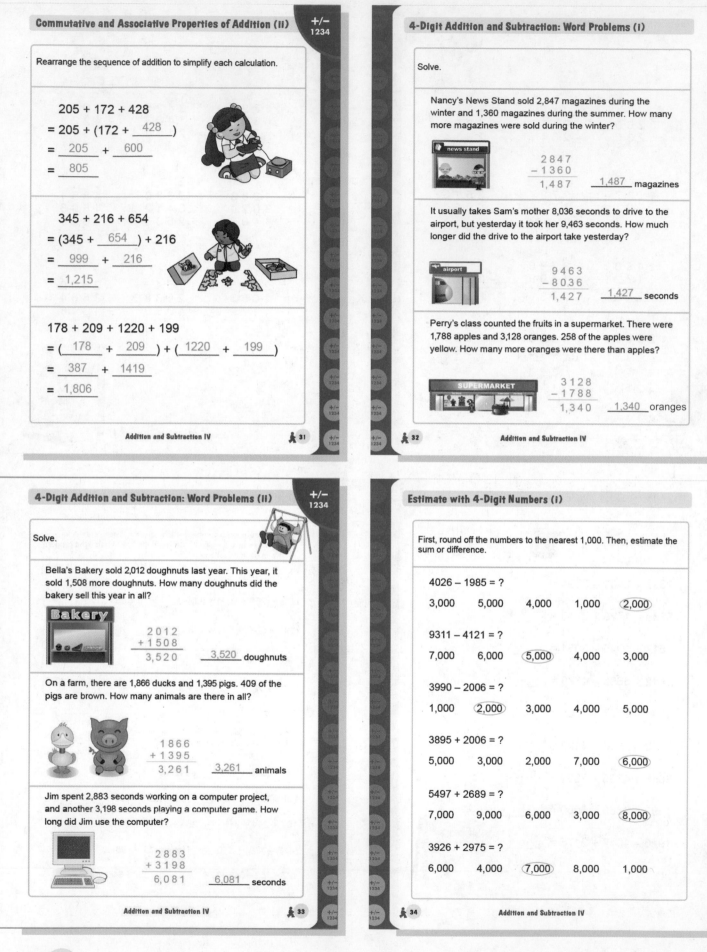

Commutative and Associative Properties of Addition (ii)

+/−
1234

Rearrange the sequence of addition to simplify each calculation.

$205 + 172 + 428$

$= 205 + (172 + \underline{428})$

$= \underline{205} + \underline{600}$

$= \underline{805}$

$345 + 216 + 654$

$= (345 + \underline{654}) + 216$

$= \underline{999} + \underline{216}$

$= \underline{1,215}$

$178 + 209 + 1220 + 199$

$= (\underline{178} + \underline{209}) + (\underline{1220} + \underline{199})$

$= \underline{387} + \underline{1419}$

$= \underline{1,806}$

Addition and Subtraction IV   🚶 31

4-Digit Addition and Subtraction: Word Problems (i)

Solve.

Nancy's News Stand sold 2,847 magazines during the winter and 1,360 magazines during the summer. How many more magazines were sold during the winter?

```
  2 8 4 7
− 1 3 6 0
  1,4 8 7     1,487 magazines
```

It usually takes Sam's mother 8,036 seconds to drive to the airport, but yesterday it took her 9,463 seconds. How much longer did the drive to the airport take yesterday?

```
  9 4 6 3
− 8 0 3 6
  1,4 2 7     1,427 seconds
```

Perry's class counted the fruits in a supermarket. There were 1,788 apples and 3,128 oranges. 258 of the apples were yellow. How many more oranges were there than apples?

```
  3 1 2 8
− 1 7 8 8
  1,3 4 0     1,340 oranges
```

🚶 32   *Addition and Subtraction IV*

4-Digit Addition and Subtraction: Word Problems (ii)

+/−
1234

Solve.

Bella's Bakery sold 2,012 doughnuts last year. This year, it sold 1,508 more doughnuts. How many doughnuts did the bakery sell this year in all?

```
  2 0 1 2
+ 1 5 0 8
  3,5 2 0     3,520 doughnuts
```

On a farm, there are 1,866 ducks and 1,395 pigs. 409 of the pigs are brown. How many animals are there in all?

```
  1 8 6 6
+ 1 3 9 5
  3,2 6 1     3,261 animals
```

Jim spent 2,883 seconds working on a computer project, and another 3,198 seconds playing a computer game. How long did Jim use the computer?

```
  2 8 8 3
+ 3 1 9 8
  6,0 8 1     6,081 seconds
```

Addition and Subtraction IV   🚶 33

Estimate with 4-Digit Numbers (i)

First, round off the numbers to the nearest 1,000. Then, estimate the sum or difference.

$4026 − 1985 = ?$

3,000   5,000   4,000   1,000   (2,000)

$9311 − 4121 = ?$

7,000   6,000   (5,000)   4,000   3,000

$3990 − 2006 = ?$

1,000   (2,000)   3,000   4,000   5,000

$3895 + 2006 = ?$

5,000   3,000   2,000   7,000   (6,000)

$5497 + 2689 = ?$

7,000   9,000   6,000   3,000   (8,000)

$3926 + 2975 = ?$

6,000   4,000   (7,000)   8,000   1,000

🚶 34   *Addition and Subtraction IV*

Answer Key

Estimate with 4-Digit Numbers (ii)

Round each number to the nearest hundred. Then, draw a ✔ in the box next to the correct answer for each problem.

Jeff has been shopping for a professional camera kit that costs about $2,500. Which one of these camera kits is closest to the total that he wants to spend?

Camera: $2,200   Flash: $190   Lens: $410 ☐

Camera: $1,750   Flash: $500   Lens: $400 ✓

Camera: $1,600   Flash: $270   Lens: $260 ☐

Camera: $1,600   Flash: $680   Lens: $500 ☐

Adrienne wants to buy a laptop and a printer. Which one of these packages should she choose if she only wants to spend about $2,100?

Laptop: $2,000   Printer: $265   ☐

Laptop: $1,800   Printer: $460   ☐

Laptop: $1,650   Printer: $450   ☐

Laptop: $1,700   Printer: $550   ☐

Laptop: $1,580   Printer: $429   ✓

Addition and Subtraction IV   35

Star Question

Solve.

Mr. Stockton took $2,000 out of the bank and bought two electric appliances. The sum of the prices was above $1,500. How much money did he have left after buying the appliances?

$1,215 $875 $1,080 $125

(Hint: Use estimation to eliminate the combinations of items that would cost less than $1,500 or more than $2.)

$$2,000 - 1,080 - 875 = 45$$

1 0 8 0	2 0 0 0
+ 8 7 5	− 1 9 5 5
1,9 5 5	4 5

$45

36   Addition and Subtraction IV

Multiply 1-Digit Numbers

Multiply.

$$\begin{array}{r} 6 \\ \times\ 7 \\ \hline 4\,2 \end{array} \qquad \begin{array}{r} 5 \\ \times\ 4 \\ \hline 2\,0 \end{array} \qquad \begin{array}{r} 3 \\ \times\ 8 \\ \hline 2\,4 \end{array} \qquad \begin{array}{r} 7 \\ \times\ 5 \\ \hline 3\,5 \end{array} \qquad \begin{array}{r} 9 \\ \times\ 6 \\ \hline 5\,4 \end{array}$$

Write an equation to match each picture.

$$2 \times 3 \quad = \quad \underline{3} \times \underline{2}$$

$$\underline{5} \times \underline{4} \quad = \quad 4 \times 5$$

Solve.

Mary bought 4 boxes of candy. There were 8 candies in each box. How many candies did Mary buy in all?

_32_ candies

40   Multiplication I

Multiply a 2-Digit Number by a 1-Digit Number (i)

Multiply.

$$\begin{array}{r} 12 \\ \times\ 1 \\ \hline 12 \end{array} \qquad \begin{array}{r} 18 \\ \times\ 1 \\ \hline 18 \end{array} \qquad \begin{array}{r} 16 \\ \times\ 1 \\ \hline 16 \end{array}$$

$$\begin{array}{r} 28 \\ \times\ 0 \\ \hline 0 \end{array} \qquad \begin{array}{r} 10 \\ \times\ 3 \\ \hline 30 \end{array} \qquad \begin{array}{r} 10 \\ \times\ 5 \\ \hline 50 \end{array}$$

$$\begin{array}{r} 10 \\ \times\ 6 \\ \hline 60 \end{array} \qquad \begin{array}{r} 10 \\ \times\ 7 \\ \hline 70 \end{array} \qquad \begin{array}{r} 42 \\ \times\ 5 \\ \hline 210 \end{array} \qquad \begin{array}{r} 23 \\ \times\ 7 \\ \hline 161 \end{array}$$

$$\begin{array}{r} 35 \\ \times\ 3 \\ \hline 105 \end{array} \qquad \begin{array}{r} 62 \\ \times\ 2 \\ \hline 124 \end{array} \qquad \begin{array}{r} 17 \\ \times\ 4 \\ \hline 68 \end{array} \qquad \begin{array}{r} 14 \\ \times\ 8 \\ \hline 112 \end{array}$$

41   Multiplication I

Multiply a 2-Digit Number by a 1-Digit Number (ii)

Multiply.

	12		23		18		26
x	6	x	5	x	9	x	7
	72		115		162		182

	33		46		15		18
x	7	x	3	x	6	x	3
	231		138		90		54

	54		72		64		47
x	2	x	3	x	6	x	3
	108		216		384		141

	54		62		23
x	5	x	3	x	6
	270		186		138

Multiply a 2-Digit Number by a 1-Digit Number (iii)

×1

Multiply.

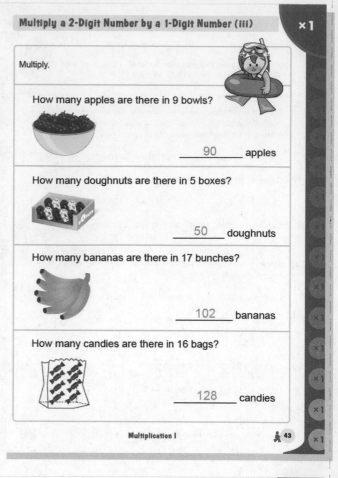

How many apples are there in 9 bowls?

__90__ apples

How many doughnuts are there in 5 boxes?

__50__ doughnuts

How many bananas are there in 17 bunches?

__102__ bananas

How many candies are there in 16 bags?

__128__ candies

Multiply a 3-Digit Number by a 1-Digit Number (i)

Multiply.

	400		200
x	2	x	2
	800		400

	400		237		158		456
x	3	x	2	x	4	x	3
	1,200		474		632		1,368

	372		512		326		159
x	2	x	4	x	5	x	6
	744		2,048		1,630		954

	123		251		397		403
x	7	x	6	x	5	x	7
	861		1,506		1,985		2,821

Multiply a 3-Digit Number by a 1-Digit Number (ii)

×1

Multiply.

	532		326		278		347
x	6	x	4	x	7	x	5
	3,192		1,304		1,946		1,735

	692		708		812		973
x	4	x	6	x	3	x	2
	2,768		4,248		2,436		1,946

	456		641		523		691
x	5	x	7	x	4	x	7
	2,280		4,487		2,092		4,837

	807		467
x	3	x	8
	2,421		3,736

Answer Key

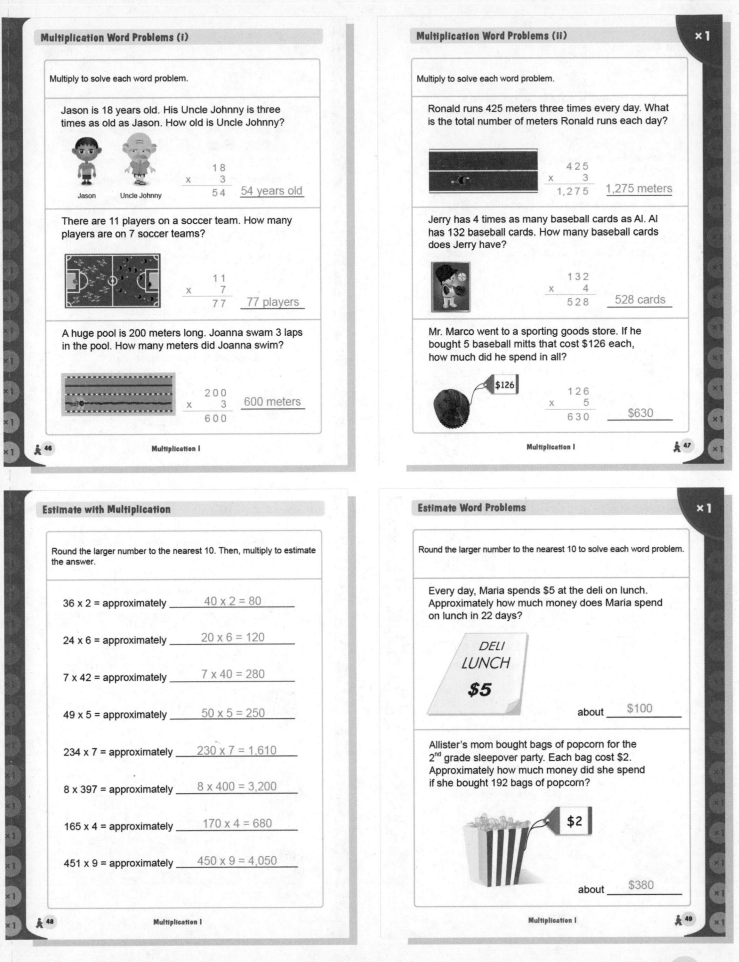

Multiplication Word Problems (i)

Multiply to solve each word problem.

Jason is 18 years old. His Uncle Johnny is three times as old as Jason. How old is Uncle Johnny?

Jason   Uncle Johnny

$$\begin{array}{r} 18 \\ \times 3 \\ \hline 54 \end{array}$$ 54 years old

There are 11 players on a soccer team. How many players are on 7 soccer teams?

$$\begin{array}{r} 11 \\ \times 7 \\ \hline 77 \end{array}$$ 77 players

A huge pool is 200 meters long. Joanna swam 3 laps in the pool. How many meters did Joanna swim?

$$\begin{array}{r} 200 \\ \times 3 \\ \hline 600 \end{array}$$ 600 meters

Multiplication Word Problems (ii)   ×1

Multiply to solve each word problem.

Ronald runs 425 meters three times every day. What is the total number of meters Ronald runs each day?

$$\begin{array}{r} 425 \\ \times 3 \\ \hline 1,275 \end{array}$$ 1,275 meters

Jerry has 4 times as many baseball cards as Al. Al has 132 baseball cards. How many baseball cards does Jerry have?

$$\begin{array}{r} 132 \\ \times 4 \\ \hline 528 \end{array}$$ 528 cards

Mr. Marco went to a sporting goods store. If he bought 5 baseball mitts that cost $126 each, how much did he spend in all?

$126

$$\begin{array}{r} 126 \\ \times 5 \\ \hline 630 \end{array}$$ $630

Estimate with Multiplication

Round the larger number to the nearest 10. Then, multiply to estimate the answer.

36 x 2 = approximately   40 x 2 = 80

24 x 6 = approximately   20 x 6 = 120

7 x 42 = approximately   7 x 40 = 280

49 x 5 = approximately   50 x 5 = 250

234 x 7 = approximately   230 x 7 = 1,610

8 x 397 = approximately   8 x 400 = 3,200

165 x 4 = approximately   170 x 4 = 680

451 x 9 = approximately   450 x 9 = 4,050

Estimate Word Problems   ×1

Round the larger number to the nearest 10 to solve each word problem.

Every day, Maria spends $5 at the deli on lunch. Approximately how much money does Maria spend on lunch in 22 days?

DELI LUNCH $5

about $100

Allister's mom bought bags of popcorn for the 2nd grade sleepover party. Each bag cost $2. Approximately how much money did she spend if she bought 192 bags of popcorn?

$2

about $380

Answer Key

Star Question

Solve.

The junior baseball team of Brockport started a fundraiser selling caps, t-shirts, and candy bars.
The team went to two locations: Boston and Amherst.

In Boston, they sold 102 caps, 246 t-shirts, and 537 candy bars.

In Amherst, they sold 78 caps, 194 t-shirts, and 673 candy bars.

Caps cost $5, t-shirts cost $8, and candy bars cost $2.

How much money did they raise?

selling caps: ___$900___

selling t-shirts: ___$3,520___

selling candy bars: ___$2,420___

in all: ___$6,840___

CHOCO-YUM!

50   Multiplication I

Divide 1- and 2-Digit Numbers

Divide.

20 squares are divided into 5 equal groups.
There are ___4___ squares in each group.

$4 \div 2 =$ ___2___ $24 \div 3 =$ ___8___

$36 \div 6 =$ ___6___ $63 \div 7 =$ ___9___

$13 \div 2$ The remainder is ___1___.

$29 \div 6$ The remainder is ___5___.

If 18 oranges were shared among 6 children, how many oranges would each child receive?

$$\begin{array}{r} 3 \\ 6\overline{)1\ 8} \\ 1\ 8 \end{array}$$ ___3___ oranges

54   Division I

Learn Short Division

$2\overline{)24}$

Follow the steps to use short division to solve the question.

$62 \div 5 = ?$

Step 1:

$$5\overline{)6\,_{1}2}$$ $\boxed{1}$

Think: 6 ÷ 5 is about 1.

Write a 1 in the tens place of the answer area.

1 times 5 is 5. 6 minus 5 is 1.

Write a 1 to the left of the 2.

Step 2:

$$\begin{array}{r} 1\,\boxed{2}\ r\ \boxed{2} \\ 5\overline{)6\,_{1}2} \end{array}$$

Think: 12 ÷ 5 is about 2.

Write a 2 in the ones place of the answer area.

2 times 5 is 10. 12 minus 10 is 2.

Then, write the remainder.

Therefore,

$62 \div 5 =$ ___12 r 2___

Division I   55

Use Short Division (i)

Use short division to solve each equation.

$$3\overline{)1\,5}^{\,5}$$

Which number multiplied by 3 equals 15?

$3\overline{)4\,9}$

Step 1	Step 2
$3\overline{)4\,_{1}9}^{\,1}$ →	$3\overline{)4\,9}^{\,16\ r\ 1}$

$5\overline{)7\,0}$

Step 1	Step 2
$5\overline{)7\,_{1}0}^{\,1}$ →	$5\overline{)7\,_{1}0}^{\,14}$

$6\overline{)9\,5}$

Step 1	Step 2
$6\overline{)9\,_{1}5}^{\,1}$ →	$6\overline{)9\,_{1}5}^{\,15\ r\ 5}$

56   Division I

Use Short Division (ii)

Use short division to solve each equation. Then, circle Mike's presents. The holiday presents whose equations have answers with a remainder of 1 belong to Mike.

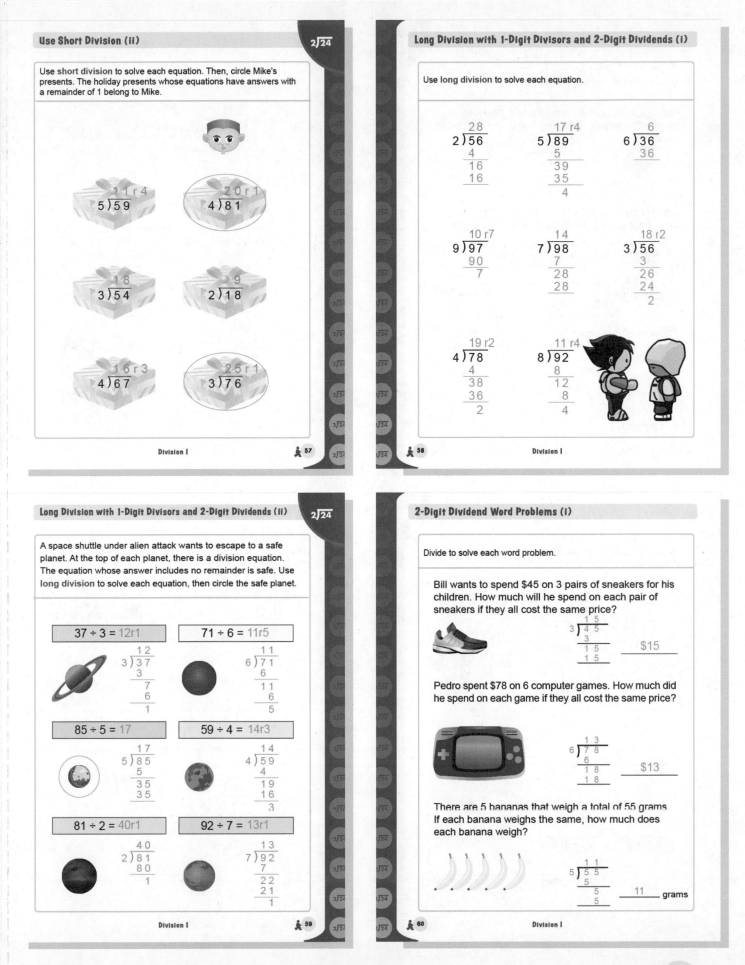

11 r 4
5⟌59

20 r 1
4⟌81

18
3⟌54

9
2⟌18

16 r 3
4⟌67

25 r 1
3⟌76

Division I   57

Long Division with 1-Digit Divisors and 2-Digit Dividends (i)

Use long division to solve each equation.

```
   28
2)56
   4
   16
   16
```

```
   17 r4
5)89
   5
   39
   35
    4
```

```
    6
6)36
   36
```

```
   10 r7
9)97
   90
    7
```

```
   14
7)98
   7
   28
   28
```

```
   18 r2
3)56
   3
   26
   24
    2
```

```
   19 r2
4)78
   4
   38
   36
    2
```

```
   11 r4
8)92
   8
   12
    8
    4
```

58   Division I

Long Division with 1-Digit Divisors and 2-Digit Dividends (ii)

A space shuttle under alien attack wants to escape to a safe planet. At the top of each planet, there is a division equation. The equation whose answer includes no remainder is safe. Use long division to solve each equation, then circle the safe planet.

37 ÷ 3 = 12r1

```
   12
3)37
   3
   7
   6
   1
```

71 ÷ 6 = 11r5

```
   11
6)71
   6
   11
    6
    5
```

85 ÷ 5 = 17

```
   17
5)85
   5
   35
   35
```

59 ÷ 4 = 14r3

```
   14
4)59
   4
   19
   16
    3
```

81 ÷ 2 = 40r1

```
   40
2)81
   80
    1
```

92 ÷ 7 = 13r1

```
   13
7)92
   7
   22
   21
    1
```

Division I   59

2-Digit Dividend Word Problems (i)

Divide to solve each word problem.

Bill wants to spend $45 on 3 pairs of sneakers for his children. How much will he spend on each pair of sneakers if they all cost the same price?

```
   15
3)45
   3
   15
   15
```
$15

Pedro spent $78 on 6 computer games. How much did he spend on each game if they all cost the same price?

```
   13
6)78
   6
   18
   18
```
$13

There are 5 bananas that weigh a total of 55 grams If each banana weighs the same, how much does each banana weigh?

```
   11
5)55
   5
   5
   5
```
11 grams

60   Division I

Answer Key   153

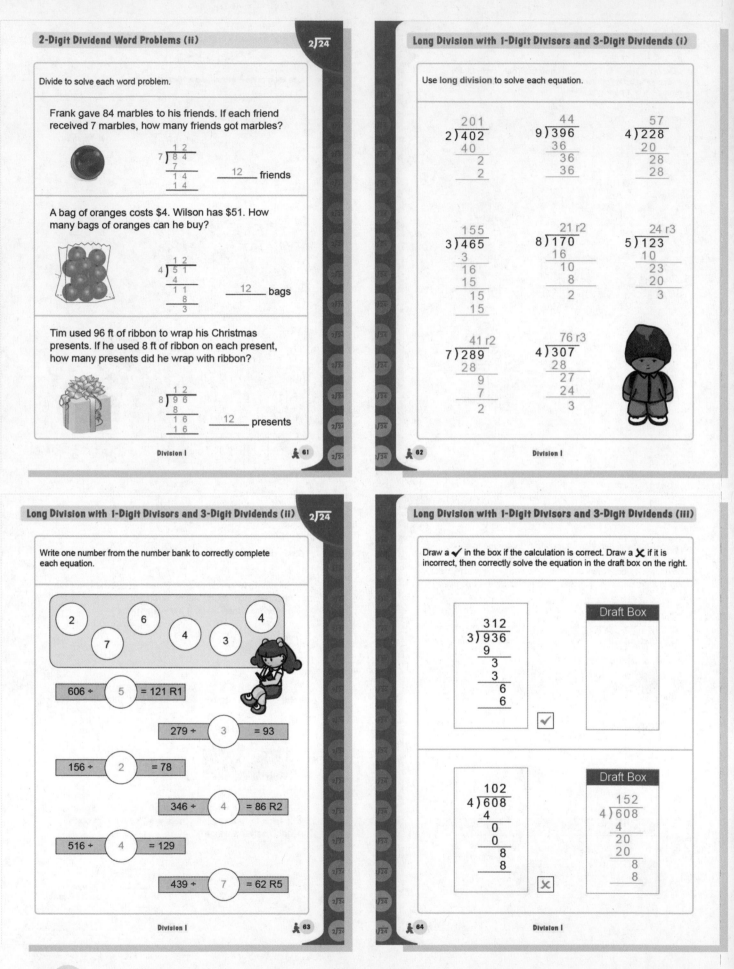

2-Digit Dividend Word Problems (ii) $2\overline{)24}$

Divide to solve each word problem.

Frank gave 84 marbles to his friends. If each friend received 7 marbles, how many friends got marbles?

$$
\begin{array}{r}
1\ 2 \\
7\overline{)8\ 4} \\
7 \\
\hline
1\ 4 \\
1\ 4 \\
\end{array}
$$

_12_ friends

A bag of oranges costs $4. Wilson has $51. How many bags of oranges can he buy?

$$
\begin{array}{r}
1\ 2 \\
4\overline{)5\ 1} \\
4 \\
\hline
1\ 1 \\
8 \\
\hline
3 \\
\end{array}
$$

_12_ bags

Tim used 96 ft of ribbon to wrap his Christmas presents. If he used 8 ft of ribbon on each present, how many presents did he wrap with ribbon?

$$
\begin{array}{r}
1\ 2 \\
8\overline{)9\ 6} \\
8 \\
\hline
1\ 6 \\
1\ 6 \\
\end{array}
$$

_12_ presents

Division I   61

Long Division with 1-Digit Divisors and 3-Digit Dividends (i)

Use long division to solve each equation.

$$
\begin{array}{r}
201 \\
2\overline{)402} \\
40 \\
\hline
2 \\
2 \\
\end{array}
\qquad
\begin{array}{r}
44 \\
9\overline{)396} \\
36 \\
\hline
36 \\
36 \\
\end{array}
\qquad
\begin{array}{r}
57 \\
4\overline{)228} \\
20 \\
\hline
28 \\
28 \\
\end{array}
$$

$$
\begin{array}{r}
155 \\
3\overline{)465} \\
3 \\
\hline
16 \\
15 \\
\hline
15 \\
15 \\
\end{array}
\qquad
\begin{array}{r}
21\ r2 \\
8\overline{)170} \\
16 \\
\hline
10 \\
8 \\
\hline
2 \\
\end{array}
\qquad
\begin{array}{r}
24\ r3 \\
5\overline{)123} \\
10 \\
\hline
23 \\
20 \\
\hline
3 \\
\end{array}
$$

$$
\begin{array}{r}
41\ r2 \\
7\overline{)289} \\
28 \\
\hline
9 \\
7 \\
\hline
2 \\
\end{array}
\qquad
\begin{array}{r}
76\ r3 \\
4\overline{)307} \\
28 \\
\hline
27 \\
24 \\
\hline
3 \\
\end{array}
$$

62   Division I

Long Division with 1-Digit Divisors and 3-Digit Dividends (ii) $2\overline{)24}$

Write one number from the number bank to correctly complete each equation.

Number bank: 2   6   4   7   4   3

606 ÷ ⑤ = 121 R1

279 ÷ ③ = 93

156 ÷ ② = 78

346 ÷ ④ = 86 R2

516 ÷ ④ = 129

439 ÷ ⑦ = 62 R5

Division I   63

Long Division with 1-Digit Divisors and 3-Digit Dividends (iii)

Draw a ✔ in the box if the calculation is correct. Draw a ✘ if it is incorrect, then correctly solve the equation in the draft box on the right.

$$
\begin{array}{r}
312 \\
3\overline{)936} \\
9 \\
\hline
3 \\
3 \\
\hline
6 \\
6 \\
\end{array}
$$

✔

Draft Box

$$
\begin{array}{r}
102 \\
4\overline{)608} \\
4 \\
\hline
0 \\
0 \\
\hline
8 \\
8 \\
\end{array}
$$

✘

Draft Box

$$
\begin{array}{r}
152 \\
4\overline{)608} \\
4 \\
\hline
20 \\
20 \\
\hline
8 \\
8 \\
\end{array}
$$

64   Division I

Answer Key

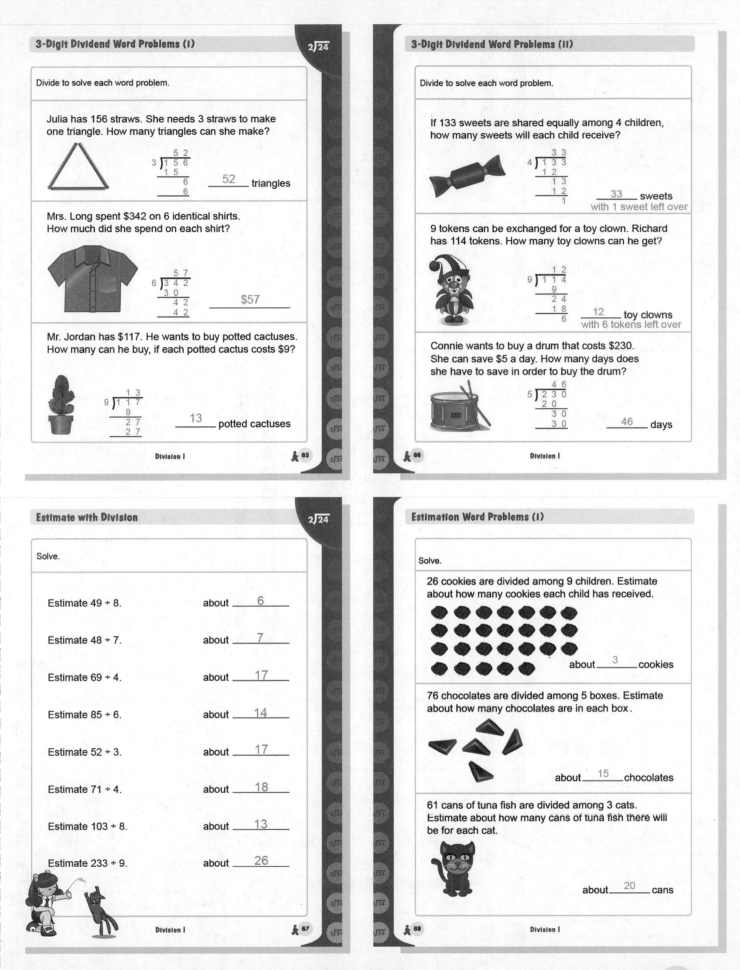

3-Digit Dividend Word Problems (I)

Divide to solve each word problem.

Julia has 156 straws. She needs 3 straws to make one triangle. How many triangles can she make?

$$3\overline{)156}$$ gives 52

_____52_____ triangles

Mrs. Long spent $342 on 6 identical shirts. How much did she spend on each shirt?

$$6\overline{)342}$$ gives 57

_____$57_____

Mr. Jordan has $117. He wants to buy potted cactuses. How many can he buy, if each potted cactus costs $9?

$$9\overline{)117}$$ gives 13

_____13_____ potted cactuses

Division I 65

3-Digit Dividend Word Problems (II)

Divide to solve each word problem.

If 133 sweets are shared equally among 4 children, how many sweets will each child receive?

$$4\overline{)133}$$ gives 33

_____33_____ sweets
with 1 sweet left over

9 tokens can be exchanged for a toy clown. Richard has 114 tokens. How many toy clowns can he get?

$$9\overline{)114}$$ gives 12

_____12_____ toy clowns
with 6 tokens left over

Connie wants to buy a drum that costs $230. She can save $5 a day. How many days does she have to save in order to buy the drum?

$$5\overline{)230}$$ gives 46

_____46_____ days

Division I 66

Estimate with Division

Solve.

Estimate 49 ÷ 8.   about _____6_____

Estimate 48 ÷ 7.   about _____7_____

Estimate 69 ÷ 4.   about _____17_____

Estimate 85 ÷ 6.   about _____14_____

Estimate 52 ÷ 3.   about _____17_____

Estimate 71 ÷ 4.   about _____18_____

Estimate 103 ÷ 8.   about _____13_____

Estimate 233 ÷ 9.   about _____26_____

Division I 67

Estimation Word Problems (I)

Solve.

26 cookies are divided among 9 children. Estimate about how many cookies each child has received.

about _____3_____ cookies

76 chocolates are divided among 5 boxes. Estimate about how many chocolates are in each box.

about _____15_____ chocolates

61 cans of tuna fish are divided among 3 cats. Estimate about how many cans of tuna fish there will be for each cat.

about _____20_____ cans

Division I 68

Answer Key

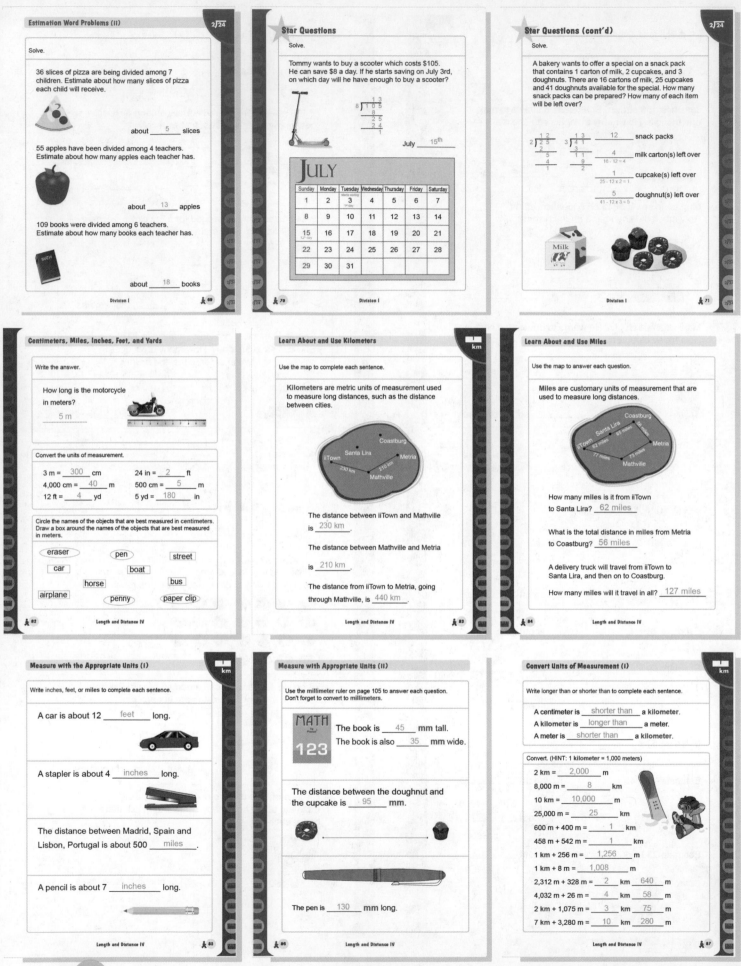

Estimation Word Problems (II)

2⟌24

Solve.

36 slices of pizza are being divided among 7 children. Estimate about how many slices of pizza each child will receive.

about ___5___ slices

55 apples have been divided among 4 teachers. Estimate about how many apples each teacher has.

about ___13___ apples

109 books were divided among 6 teachers. Estimate about how many books each teacher has.

about ___18___ books

Division I   69

★ Star Questions

Solve.

Tommy wants to buy a scooter which costs $105. He can save $8 a day. If he starts saving on July 3rd, on which day will he have enough to buy a scooter?

```
     1 3
8 ) 1 0 5
    8
    2 5
    2 4
    1
```

July ___15th___

JULY

Sunday	Monday	Tuesday	Wednesday	Thursday	Friday	Saturday
1	2	3 starts saving 1st day	4	5	6	7
8	9	10	11	12	13	14
15 13th day	16	17	18	19	20	21
22	23	24	25	26	27	28
29	30	31				

70   Division I

★ Star Questions (cont'd)

2⟌24

Solve.

A bakery wants to offer a special on a snack pack that contains 1 carton of milk, 2 cupcakes, and 3 doughnuts. There are 16 cartons of milk, 25 cupcakes and 41 doughnuts available for the special. How many snack packs can be prepared? How many of each item will be left over?

```
     1 2          1 3
2 ) 2 5        3 ) 4 1
    2              3
    5              1 1
    4              9
    1              2
```

___12___ snack packs

___4___ milk carton(s) left over
16 - 12 = 4

___1___ cupcake(s) left over
25 - 12 x 2 = 1

___5___ doughnut(s) left over
41 - 12 x 3 = 5

Milk

Division I   71

Centimeters, Miles, Inches, Feet, and Yards

Write the answer.

How long is the motorcycle in meters?

___5 m___

Convert the units of measurement.

3 m = ___300___ cm   24 in = ___2___ ft
4,000 cm = ___40___ m   500 cm = ___5___ m
12 ft = ___4___ yd   5 yd = ___180___ in

Circle the names of the objects that are best measured in centimeters. Draw a box around the names of the objects that are best measured in meters.

(eraser)   (pen)   [street]
[car]   [boat]
        (horse)   [bus]
(airplane)   (penny)   (paper clip)

82   Length and Distance IV

Learn About and Use Kilometers

km

Use the map to complete each sentence.

Kilometers are metric units of measurement used to measure long distances, such as the distance between cities.

Coastburg
Santa Lira   Metria
iiTown
230 km   210 km
Mathville

The distance between iiTown and Mathville is ___230 km___.

The distance between Mathville and Metria is ___210 km___.

The distance from iiTown to Metria, going through Mathville, is ___440 km___.

Length and Distance IV   83

Learn About and Use Miles

Use the map to answer each question.

Miles are customary units of measurement that are used to measure long distances.

Coastburg
Santa Lira   56 miles
iiTown   65 miles   Metria
62 miles   73 miles
77 miles   Mathville

How many miles is it from iiTown to Santa Lira? ___62 miles___

What is the total distance in miles from Metria to Coastburg? ___56 miles___

A delivery truck will travel from iiTown to Santa Lira, and then on to Coastburg.

How many miles will it travel in all? ___127 miles___

84   Length and Distance IV

Measure with the Appropriate Units (I)

km

Write inches, feet, or miles to complete each sentence.

A car is about 12 ___feet___ long.

A stapler is about 4 ___inches___ long.

The distance between Madrid, Spain and Lisbon, Portugal is about 500 ___miles___.

A pencil is about 7 ___inches___ long.

Length and Distance IV   85

Measure with Appropriate Units (II)

Use the millimeter ruler on page 105 to answer each question. Don't forget to convert to millimeters.

MATH
123

The book is ___45___ mm tall.
The book is also ___35___ mm wide.

The distance between the doughnut and the cupcake is ___95___ mm.

The pen is ___130___ mm long.

86   Length and Distance IV

Convert Units of Measurement (I)

km

Write longer than or shorter than to complete each sentence.

A centimeter is ___shorter than___ a kilometer.
A kilometer is ___longer than___ a meter.
A meter is ___shorter than___ a kilometer.

Convert. (HINT: 1 kilometer = 1,000 meters)

2 km = ___2,000___ m		
8,000 m = ___8___ km		
10 km = ___10,000___ m		
25,000 m = ___25___ km		
600 m + 400 m = ___1___ km		
458 m + 542 m = ___1___ km		
1 km + 256 m = ___1,256___ m		
1 km + 8 m = ___1,008___ m		
2,312 m + 328 m = ___2___ km ___640___ m		
4,032 m + 26 m = ___4___ km ___58___ m		
2 km + 1,075 m = ___3___ km ___75___ m		
7 km + 3,280 m = ___10___ km ___280___ m		

Length and Distance IV   87

Answer Key

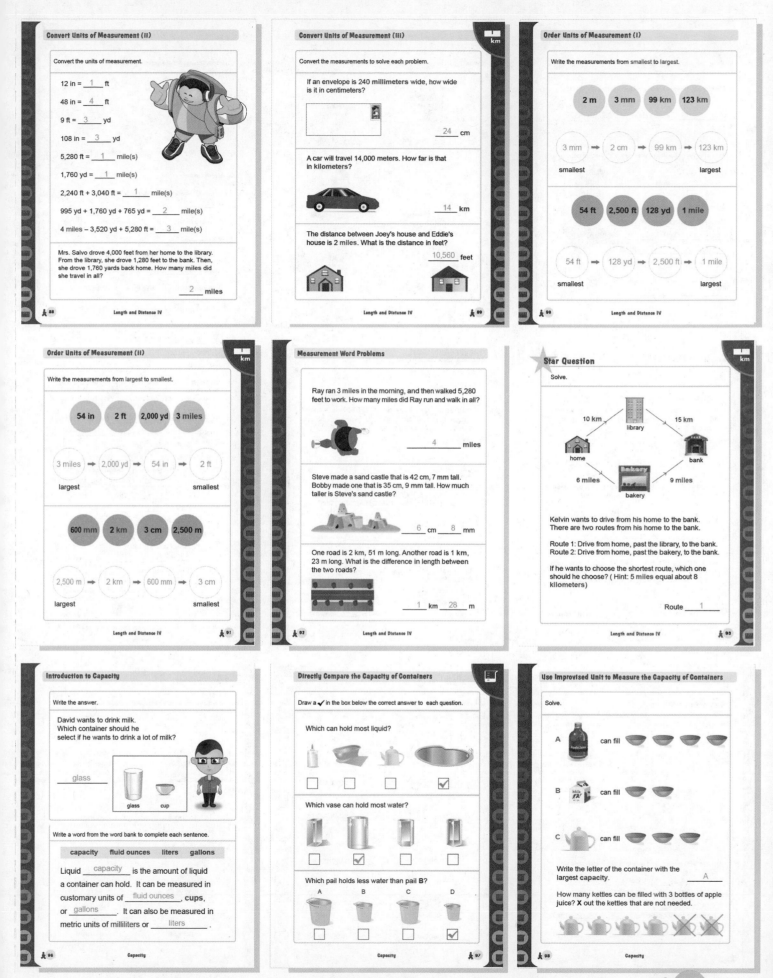

Convert Units of Measurement (II)

Convert the units of measurement.

12 in = __1__ ft

48 in = __4__ ft

9 ft = __3__ yd

108 in = __3__ yd

5,280 ft = __1__ mile(s)

1,760 yd = __1__ mile(s)

2,240 ft + 3,040 ft = __1__ mile(s)

995 yd + 1,760 yd + 765 yd = __2__ mile(s)

4 miles – 3,520 yd + 5,280 ft = __3__ mile(s)

Mrs. Salvo drove 4,000 feet from her home to the library. From the library, she drove 1,280 feet to the bank. Then, she drove 1,760 yards back home. How many miles did she travel in all?

__2__ miles

88   Length and Distance IV

Convert Units of Measurement (III)

Convert the measurements to solve each problem.

If an envelope is 240 millimeters wide, how wide is it in centimeters?

__24__ cm

A car will travel 14,000 meters. How far is that in kilometers?

__14__ km

The distance between Joey's house and Eddie's house is 2 miles. What is the distance in feet?

__10,560__ feet

Length and Distance IV   89

Order Units of Measurement (I)

Write the measurements from smallest to largest.

2 m   3 mm   99 km   123 km

3 mm → 2 cm → 99 km → 123 km
smallest   largest

54 ft   2,500 ft   128 yd   1 mile

54 ft → 128 yd → 2,500 ft → 1 mile
smallest   largest

90   Length and Distance IV

Order Units of Measurement (II)

Write the measurements from largest to smallest.

54 in   2 ft   2,000 yd   3 miles

3 miles → 2,000 yd → 54 in → 2 ft
largest   smallest

600 mm   2 km   3 cm   2,500 m

2,500 m → 2 km → 600 mm → 3 cm
largest   smallest

Length and Distance IV   91

Measurement Word Problems

Ray ran 3 miles in the morning, and then walked 5,280 feet to work. How many miles did Ray run and walk in all?

__4__ miles

Steve made a sand castle that is 42 cm, 7 mm tall. Bobby made one that is 35 cm, 9 mm tall. How much taller is Steve's sand castle?

__6__ cm __8__ mm

One road is 2 km, 51 m long. Another road is 1 km, 23 m long. What is the difference in length between the two roads?

__1__ km __28__ m

92   Length and Distance IV

Star Question

Solve.

10 km — library — 15 km
home   bank
6 miles — bakery — 9 miles

Kelvin wants to drive from his home to the bank. There are two routes from his home to the bank.

Route 1: Drive from home, past the library, to the bank.
Route 2: Drive from home, past the bakery, to the bank.

If he wants to choose the shortest route, which one should he choose? (Hint: 5 miles equal about 8 kilometers)

Route __1__

Length and Distance IV   93

Introduction to Capacity

Write the answer.

David wants to drink milk. Which container should he select if he wants to drink a lot of milk?

__glass__

glass   cup

Write a word from the word bank to complete each sentence.

| capacity | fluid ounces | liters | gallons |

Liquid __capacity__ is the amount of liquid a container can hold. It can be measured in customary units of __fluid ounces__, **cups**, or __gallons__. It can also be measured in metric units of milliliters or __liters__.

96   Capacity

Directly Compare the Capacity of Containers

Draw a ✔ in the box below the correct answer to each question.

Which can hold most liquid?

☐ ☐ ☐ ☑

Which vase can hold most water?

☐ ☑ ☐ ☐

Which pail holds less water than pail B?

A   B   C   D

☐ ☐ ☐ ☑

Capacity   97

Use Improvised Unit to Measure the Capacity of Containers

Solve.

A can fill (4 bowls)

B can fill (2 bowls)

C can fill (3 bowls)

Write the letter of the container with the largest capacity. __A__

How many kettles can be filled with 3 bottles of apple juice? X out the kettles that are not needed.

(kettles, last two X'd out)

98   Capacity

Measure, then write the answers.

Measure the capacity of your sink with a coffee cup.

__(answer will vary)__ coffee cups

Measure the capacity of your sink with a soup pot.

__(answer will vary)__ pots

Which number is larger? Why?

The first number is bigger

because the liquid capacity of

a coffee cup is smaller than a

soup pot.

Capacity   99

Write fl oz, c, gal, mL, or L to correctly complete each measurement.

1 __gal__ of paint

1 __c__ of coffee

$\frac{1}{7}$ __mL__ of water

2 __L__ of soda

1 __L__ of milk

12 __fl oz__ of iced tea

100   Capacity

Circle the container with the largest capacity.

capacity = 20 c   capacity = 1 gal

Circle each answer.

The total capacity of 4 cans of soda at 12 fl oz each

is _____ 1 L.

(more than)   less than

26 c is _____ 2 gal.

more than   (less than)   the same as

4 gal is _____ 512 fl oz.

more than   less than   (the same as)

Capacity   101

Write the answers.

A bowl can hold 2 cups of soup. A soup pot can hold 15 bowls of soup. How many cups does it take to fill the soup pot?

__30__ cups

If 4 identical vases can hold 3 liters of water combined, how many liters can 12 of these vases hold?

__9__ liters

Kevin drinks 4 glasses of milk each day. One glass can hold 10 fluid ounces of milk. How many fluid ounces of milk does Kevin drink in two weeks?

__560__ fluid ounces

102   Capacity

Write the answers.

A jug of pear juice has a capacity of 5,630 mL. A can of pear juice has a capacity of 2 L. How much more juice can a jug hold than a can?

__3,630 mL__

A glass can hold 22 fluid ounces of lemonade. A pitcher can hold 5 glasses of lemonade. How many fluid ounces does it take to fill up half the pitcher?

__55__ fluid ounces

A tub can hold 54 gallons of water. A pool can hold 4 tubs of water. How many gallons of water does it take to fill half the pool?

__108__ gallons

Capacity   103

Write 3 gallon or 5 gallon to correctly complete the sentences that tell how to measure out 4 gallons of water using only a 3 gallon bucket and a 5 gallon bucket.

Step 1: Fill the __5 gallon__ bucket with water.

Step 2: Pour the water into the __3 gallon__ bucket until it is full.

Step 3: Empty the __3 gallon__ bucket.

Step 4: Pour the remaining 2 gallons of water left in the __5 gallon__ bucket into the __3 gallon__ bucket.

Step 5: Fill the __5 gallon__ bucket with water again.

Step 6: Pour the water into the __3 gallon__ bucket until it is full.

Now the __5 gallon__ bucket contains 4 gallons of water.

104   Capacity

Circle the equilateral triangle.

Circle the isosceles triangle.

Write one word from the word bank to complete each sentence.

acute	**three**	obtuse

All triangles have __three__ angles.

A triangle cannot have two __obtuse__ angles.

Some triangles have three __acute__ angles.

112   Triangles

Write the number of triangles found in each 3D shape.

__2__ triangle(s)

__6__ triangle(s)

__4__ triangle(s)

__4__ triangle(s)

__2__ triangle(s)

__0__ triangle(s)

Triangles   113

Write the type of triangle each sticker is shaped like.

Isosceles triangle

equilateral triangle

right-angled triangle

scalene triangle

114   Triangles

Answer Key

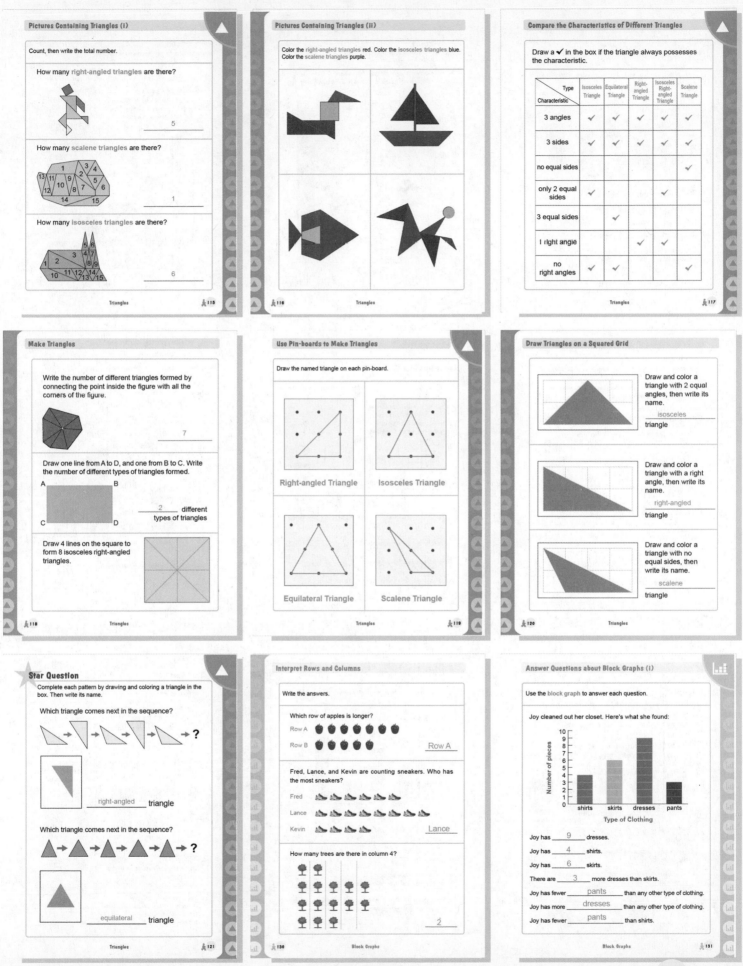

Pictures Containing Triangles (i)

Count, then write the total number.

How many right-angled triangles are there?

5

How many scalene triangles are there?

1

How many isosceles triangles are there?

6

Pictures Containing Triangles (ii)

Color the right-angled triangles red. Color the isosceles triangles blue. Color the scalene triangles purple.

Compare the Characteristics of Different Triangles

Draw a ✓ in the box if the triangle always possesses the characteristic.

Characteristic \ Type	Isosceles Triangle	Equilateral Triangle	Right-angled Triangle	Isosceles Right-angled Triangle	Scalene Triangle
3 angles	✓	✓	✓	✓	✓
3 sides	✓	✓	✓	✓	✓
no equal sides					✓
only 2 equal sides	✓			✓	
3 equal sides		✓			
1 right angle			✓	✓	
no right angles	✓	✓			✓

Make Triangles

Write the number of different triangles formed by connecting the point inside the figure with all the corners of the figure.

7

Draw one line from A to D, and one from B to C. Write the number of different types of triangles formed.

A   B

C   D

2 different types of triangles

Draw 4 lines on the square to form 8 isosceles right-angled triangles.

Use Pin-boards to Make Triangles

Draw the named triangle on each pin-board.

Right-angled Triangle

Isosceles Triangle

Equilateral Triangle

Scalene Triangle

Draw Triangles on a Squared Grid

Draw and color a triangle with 2 equal angles, then write its name.

isosceles triangle

Draw and color a triangle with a right angle, then write its name.

right-angled triangle

Draw and color a triangle with no equal sides, then write its name.

scalene triangle

★ Star Question

Complete each pattern by drawing and coloring a triangle in the box. Then write its name.

Which triangle comes next in the sequence?

→ ?

right-angled triangle

Which triangle comes next in the sequence?

△ → △ → △ → △ → △ → ?

equilateral triangle

Interpret Rows and Columns

Write the answers.

Which row of apples is longer?

Row A

Row B

Row A

Fred, Lance, and Kevin are counting sneakers. Who has the most sneakers?

Fred

Lance

Kevin

Lance

How many trees are there in column 4?

2

Answer Questions about Block Graphs (i)

Use the block graph to answer each question.

Joy cleaned out her closet. Here's what she found:

Joy has 9 dresses.

Joy has 4 shirts.

Joy has 6 skirts.

There are 3 more dresses than skirts.

Joy has fewer pants than any other type of clothing.

Joy has more dresses than any other type of clothing.

Joy has fewer pants than shirts.

Answer Key

Answer Questions about Block Graphs (ii)

Use the block graph to answer each question.

Sam, Adam, Tamara, and Crystal collected postcards from around the world.

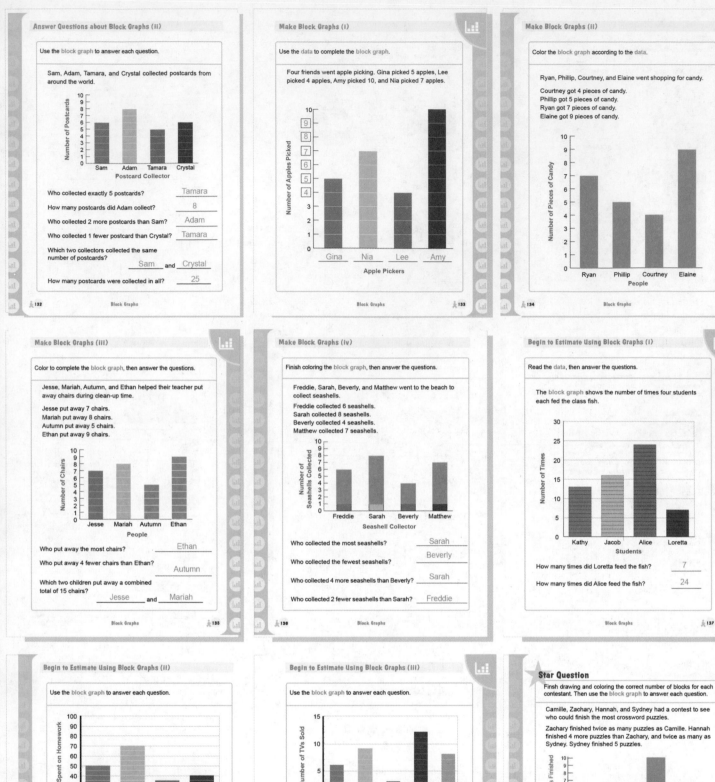

Who collected exactly 5 postcards? _Tamara_

How many postcards did Adam collect? _8_

Who collected 2 more postcards than Sam? _Adam_

Who collected 1 fewer postcard than Crystal? _Tamara_

Which two collectors collected the same number of postcards? _Sam_ and _Crystal_

How many postcards were collected in all? _25_

132   Block Graphs

Make Block Graphs (i)

Use the data to complete the block graph.

Four friends went apple picking. Gina picked 5 apples, Lee picked 4 apples, Amy picked 10, and Nia picked 7 apples.

Block Graphs   133

Make Block Graphs (ii)

Color the block graph according to the data.

Ryan, Phillip, Courtney, and Elaine went shopping for candy.

Courtney got 4 pieces of candy.
Phillip got 5 pieces of candy.
Ryan got 7 pieces of candy.
Elaine got 9 pieces of candy.

134   Block Graphs

Make Block Graphs (iii)

Color to complete the block graph, then answer the questions.

Jesse, Mariah, Autumn, and Ethan helped their teacher put away chairs during clean-up time.

Jesse put away 7 chairs.
Mariah put away 8 chairs.
Autumn put away 5 chairs.
Ethan put away 9 chairs.

Who put away the most chairs? _Ethan_

Who put away 4 fewer chairs than Ethan? _Autumn_

Which two children put away a combined total of 15 chairs? _Jesse_ and _Mariah_

Block Graphs   135

Make Block Graphs (iv)

Finish coloring the block graph, then answer the questions.

Freddie, Sarah, Beverly, and Matthew went to the beach to collect seashells.

Freddie collected 6 seashells.
Sarah collected 8 seashells.
Beverly collected 4 seashells.
Matthew collected 7 seashells.

Who collected the most seashells? _Sarah_

Who collected the fewest seashells? _Beverly_

Who collected 4 more seashells than Beverly? _Sarah_

Who collected 2 fewer seashells than Sarah? _Freddie_

136   Block Graphs

Begin to Estimate Using Block Graphs (i)

Read the data, then answer the questions.

The block graph shows the number of times four students each fed the class fish.

How many times did Loretta feed the fish? _7_

How many times did Alice feed the fish? _24_

Block Graphs   137

Begin to Estimate Using Block Graphs (ii)

Use the block graph to answer each question.

How many minutes did Martina spend on her homework? _40_

How many more minutes did Martina spend on homework than Mario? _5_

138   Block Graphs

Begin to Estimate Using Block Graphs (iii)

Use the block graph to answer each question.

How many TVs were sold during the week? _38_

How many TVs were sold on Thursday? _12_

How many TVs were sold on Tuesday and Wednesday combined? _12_

Were more TVs sold on Monday and Thursday combined or Tuesday and Wednesday combined? _Monday and Thursday combined_

Block Graphs   139

★ Star Question

Finish drawing and coloring the correct number of blocks for each contestant. Then use the block graph to answer each question.

Camille, Zachary, Hannah, and Sydney had a contest to see who could finish the most crossword puzzles.

Zachary finished twice as many puzzles as Camille. Hannah finished 4 more puzzles than Zachary, and twice as many as Sydney. Sydney finished 5 puzzles.

Who won the contest? _Hannah_

Which two contestants finished a combined total of 16 crossword puzzles? _Hannah_ and _Zachary_

The group split up into pairs. Which set of two people completed 2 more puzzles than the other set? _Hannah_ and _Camille_

140   Block Graphs

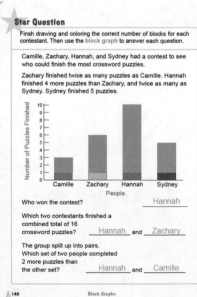

Answer Key

Stickers!

Star Performance!

You are ready for the next level!

Excellent!

I just love adding and subtracting!

WOW!

Yeah!

You are really on the ball!

Hooray for numbers!

AWESOME!

Yo-Yo! That was great!

Cool Dude!

SUPER solver!

COOL!

Great!

Congratulations! You did a fabulous job!